ERIC BRUTON

Dictionary of
Clocks and Watches

★

BONANZA BOOKS · NEW YORK

INTRODUCTION

CLOCKS rule every moment of our lives. We cannot escape them. We even live upon one—the Earth, our basic timekeeper. By its regular daily rotation, it controls the daylight and therefore the time to work and the time to sleep. Another of Nature's clocks—the Moon—records the months. A biological clock inside every one of us controls our living habits.

These are all natural clocks, and Man soon harnessed one to improve his timekeeping. He measured the moving shadows caused by the Earth's rotation. As soon as he began to live a community life, however, he found Nature's clocks insufficient and he tried to invent some of his own. The first successful artificial clocks worked by water, but the best came later and were mechanical.

The history of mechanical clocks goes back over seven centuries. The history of the watch—man's first attempt, perhaps, at what is now called precision engineering—extends for four centuries.

Nearly all other branches of engineering owe something to clockmaking; for example, the thermostat in an oven, the chain drive of a dredger, and the differential gear in the back axle of a motor-car, were all first invented for use in clocks.

Clocks and watches are also intimately linked with adventure and discovery. The only way a ship's captain could find his way across unknown oceans was by a time check. Captain Cook's timekeepers, and the chronometer Captain Bligh struggled to obtain from the mutineers of *The Bounty* before being set adrift in an open boat, are still in existence after many astonishing adventures of their own. It is so easy today to obtain 'the right time' from a wrist-watch, a radio time signal, or a TV

5

clock, that the centuries of endeavour to make the time readily available are largely forgotten.

A few hundred years ago, most of the top scientists and thinkers as well as practical clockmakers devoted their lives to the problem, such men as Galileo, Robert Hooke, and Christiaan Huygens. Even King George III of England and one of the Kings of France took lessons in the subject. The popularity of the 'Five Centuries of British Timekeeping' and 'From Pendulum to Atom' Exhibitions at Goldsmiths Hall, London, showed that the layman has the same latent interest today. Progress in precision timekeeping has never been more rapid or more important than in the twentieth century space age with its quartz crystal, molecular, and atomic clocks.

This illustrated dictionary covers the subject of timekeeping in all its aspects, from the earliest known history to the very latest inventions, some of which are as exciting as any of the past. Some of the subject is technical. That cannot be altered. But an effort has been made to avoid unnecessary technical jargon and also to include locations of interesting clocks and watches so that the reader can see them for himself.

I would like to thank Dr F. A. B. Ward, Keeper of the Time Measurement Department of the Science Museum, London, for reading the manuscript with a keen eye, and N.A.G. Press Ltd, publishers of *Horological Journal*, for their considerable help with illustrations for the plates.

ERIC BRUTON

A DICTIONARY OF
CLOCKS AND WATCHES

(All words in CAPITAL LETTERS in the text, as well as those
in **bold type,** cross refer to other entries.)

Abbot Horne Collection   Collection of over 70 SAND-GLASSES
presented to the SCIENCE MUSEUM, London, in 1952.

Accumulator Watch   Swiss ELECTRIC WATCH driven from an
accumulator in the back of the case. The accumulator lasts nine
months and can be recharged in a few hours from an ordinary
torch battery by using a special connector to a plug on the
wrist-watch.

Accuracy of Clocks   Timekeeping of mechanical clocks with
VERGE and FOLIOT or bar BALANCE made around 1500 varied by
about $\pm\frac{1}{2}$ hr. or more daily. This was brought down to $\frac{1}{4}$ hr.
by the hog's BRISTLE REGULATOR and to about 30 sec. a day by
the CROSS BEAT ESCAPEMENT in special clocks after 1586. The
BRACKET CLOCK with VERGE and BOB PENDULUM (after 1657)
would keep to ± 20 sec. daily over short periods. The SECONDS
PENDULUM with ANCHOR ESCAPEMENT (after 1671) increased
accuracy to ± 10 sec. a day and, if well regulated, to less than
± 3 sec. a week. A modern factory electric MASTER CLOCK will
hold about $\pm\frac{1}{2}$ sec. a week. A MARINE CHRONOMETER will hold
about 0.3 sec. a day. A RIEFLER CLOCK will keep to about
1/100th sec. a day. A FREE PENDULUM observatory clock is
accurate to 1 sec. a year. The QUARTZ CLOCK is accurate to
the equivalent of a second in 30 years, and the ATOMIC clock to
the equivalent of 1 sec. in 3,000 years.

7

Accuracy of Watches Watches are inherently less accurate than clocks because they are moved about, which causes POSITIONAL ERRORS. Early VERGE watches could not be relied upon within quarter of an hour. The HAIRSPRING brought accuracy down to minutes. Modern precision pocket watches should go within 5 to 10 sec. a day and precision wrist-watches to within 10 to 20 sec. Cheap watches should be within 3 to 5 min. for pocket and 5 to 10 min. for wrist. *See* **Rate** *and* **Rating Certificate.** The accuracy of timekeepers is taken for granted. Yet one that is 10 sec. a day fast or slow is 99.99% accurate. Speedometers are commonly 5% out, which with a clock would mean an error of 8 hr. 24 min. in a week!

Act of Parliament Clock Name given to COACHING or TAVERN CLOCKS when a TAX was put on timekeepers in the eighteenth century. Villagers thought it cheaper to use the inn's coaching clock—but it was not always so, as landlords employed their clocks to attract custom! (Fig. 29).

Adjusted Some watches have this word engraved on their MOVEMENTS. It means that they are high grade and have been corrected for TEMPERATURE ERRORS and for POSITIONAL ERRORS. An adjusted pendulum clock is corrected for temperature error only.

Adjuster Highly skilled man who can regulate watches to very fine limits by manipulating the HAIRSPRING, BALANCE, and parts of the ESCAPEMENT.

Ahaz, Dial of Sundial (probably the shadow of a pillar that moved up steps as the sun rose) mentioned in the Bible, II Kings, Chap. 20, verse 11.

Air Almanac Airman's equivalent of the NAUTICAL ALMANAC, giving star positions every ten min. to obtain 'fixes' for finding his position with the aid of a CHRONOMETER. Published by H.M. Stationery Office. *See* **Navigation.**

Airy, George Biddell The ASTRONOMER ROYAL from 1835–81. Discovered that if a PENDULUM or BALANCE AND SPRING is IMPULSED briefly in the mid-point of its swing, this will have least effect on its timekeeping. If the impulse is given before dead centre, the pendulum or balance will go faster, and if given after dead centre, it will go slower. There is no need to impulse at every swing. He was inventor of the ESCAPEMENT of a SIDEREAL CLOCK by Dent, for GREENWICH OBSERVATORY in 1872. Also introduced the TAPE CHRONOGRAPH to Greenwich.

Alarm Clock that can be set to ring a bell at a given time. Alarms, or 'alarums', were made as early as the fourteenth century, and many early CHAMBER CLOCKS have alarm mechanisms. Manufacture of alarms today is highly automated; one of the Scottish factories can turn them out at the rate of one every two and a half sec., automatically adjusted to an accuracy finer than many scientific instruments. Common alarms have THIRTY-HOUR MOVEMENTS. TRAVELLING CLOCKS have EIGHT-DAY alarm movements. There are modern alarms with adjustable loudness, MUSICAL ALARMS, and REPEATER ALARMS.

Alarm Watch Modern wrist-watch that incorporates an alarm mechanism for reminding the wearer of appointments, or waking him. The first was the 'Cricket'. There is a separate button for winding and setting the alarm. Some models are scaled as ELAPSED TIME INDICATORS for car parking. Others, on watches for skin divers, indicate safe underwater time limits.

Albion 'All-by-one'—all made by one man. Name falsely given to an astronomical clock made by Richard of Wallingford and placed in the south transept of St Albans Abbey in the fourteenth century. Actually a geometrical instrument he constructed.

Altitude Sundial   Type of PORTABLE SUNDIAL showing the time by the height or altitude of the sun in the sky. (The shadow of an upright post is shortest at noon when the sun is at its highest.)

American Clock   English, Dutch, French and other clock-makers were among early emigrants to North America and their own styles merged into others that became peculiarly American. *See* **Banjo Clock, Terry, U.S.A. Horological Industry, Waggon Spring Clock.**

American Watchmakers Institute   Organization of all watch-makers in the U.S.A. formed in 1960 by the amalgamation of the Horological Institute of America and the United Horo-logical Association of America. Official journal: *The American Horologist.* Address: 10525 Puritan Avenue, Detroit 38, Michigan.

Ammonia Maser   An ELECTRONIC CLOCK, in which the time-keeping element is the vibration of the ammonia molecule, developed particularly in the U.S.A. and Switzerland. Not inherently as accurate as the ATOMIC CLOCK. 'Maser' means Microwave Amplification by Simulated Emission of Radiation.

Anagram   In earlier centuries scientists established claims to discoveries and inventions by concealing them in anagrams. HOOKE's law of the BALANCE SPRING, 'as the tension is, so is the force', was concealed as 'c e i i i n o s s s t t a v', the letters comprising the Latin version 'ut tensio, sic vis'. Galileo, Newton, Huygens and others used anagrams. Sir Christopher Wren's anagram for FINDING THE LONGITUDE, still held by The Royal Society, has never been cracked!

Anchor Escapement Clock control, probably invented by Robert HOOKE or William CLEMENT of London about 1671.

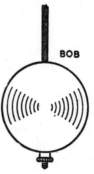

Fig. 1. Anchor escapement.

Supplanted the VERGE ESCAPEMENT and made really accurate clocks possible. Used on most pendulum clocks today. An anchor-shaped piece of steel is swung to and fro by the PENDULUM to release a tooth of the ESCAPE WHEEL at each swing, or BEAT. At the same time, the escape wheel IMPULSES the pendulum through the anchor escapement to keep it swinging. Also called the 'RECOIL ESCAPEMENT'.

Anne Boleyn Clock Clock of lantern type, said to have been given to Anne Boleyn by King Henry VIII on their wedding in

11

1532, now in the library at Windsor Castle. The elaborate copper gilt case and bracket on which it stands are excellently preserved. The MOVEMENT was replaced in mid-sixteenth century. On top of the case is a model lion with the arms of England. The two weights are engraved with the initials 'H' and 'A' and true lovers' knots. The clock was later given to Horace Walpole and was bought after his death by Queen Victoria.

Anniversary Clock   Another name for a YEAR CLOCK.

Antiquarian Horological Society   Formed in 1953 to assist and stimulate original research and preserve records and fine examples of clock and watchmaking and DIALLING. Holds regular meetings and visits to places of horological interest. Address: 35 Northampton Square, London, E.C.1.

Apparent Time   Another name for SOLAR TIME, or time as indicated by the SUNDIAL.

Appointments Clock   Device for jogging the memory. One of the earliest was Davidson's memorandum clock of 1891. There was a drum on top with slots marked in hours into which the owner put ivory tablets on which he had written his appointments. The clock delivered each tablet into a little box at the appointed hour and rang an alarm bell. A modern version is a desk pad with hours marked down one side. A built-in clock moves an indicator down the list of appointments.

Apprentice   The CLOCKMAKERS COMPANY indentured apprentices from 1631. They had to serve seven years before becoming JOURNEYMEN. A MASTER clockmaker could take a second apprentice only after the first one had served five years. The Company has published a list of apprentices which helps to trace makers. Today the BRITISH HOROLOGICAL INSTITUTE handles most indentures.

Arabic Numerals Introduced to Europe after the more literate Crusaders found Arabic numbers much more convenient than Roman, in the twelfth century, but not common on clocks until recent times.

Arbor Horological name for a shaft or axle in a clock or watch. That for the BALANCE is called the 'Staff'.

Arc The full angle through which a PENDULUM or BALANCE swings. For a precision pendulum this is usually less than $1\frac{1}{2}°$ (*see* **Circular Error**). Short pendulums may have arcs as wide as 30°. A balance normally swings through $1\frac{1}{2}$ to $1\frac{3}{4}$ turns, but this falls off to about $1\frac{1}{4}$ turns after the MAINSPRING POWER OUTPUT has fallen when the spring has run for 24 hours (*see* **Positional Errors**). Good balance action is called 'long arcs' and poor action 'short arcs'.

Arch Dial Square clock DIAL with an almost semi-circular arch in the top. The space in the arch was first used for the maker's name, or decoration, and later for AUTOMATA, or a phase of the MOON DIAL. In fashion from about 1720. Correctly a 'broken arch dial' as the arch does not extend to the edges of the dial (Plate 2).

Architectural Clock Style of case based on architectural of buildings. Earliest wooden BRACKET and LONG CASE clock CASES were made in this style.

Armillary Sphere Fixed model of the Universe made of metal rings in use from over 2,000 years ago. There is one in Pickering Court, off St James's Street, London, S.W.1. The emblem of the BRITISH HOROLOGICAL INSTITUTE.

Arnold, John (1736–99) Gunsmith who became a fine watchmaker. Made one of the world's SMALLEST WATCHES, a RING

WATCH, for King George III. Later devoted himself in London to pocket and MARINE CHRONOMETERS, patenting a BALANCE SPRING that was ISOCHRONOUS and a DETENT ESCAPEMENT. Made about 1,000 timekeepers, mostly marine, and never two alike. Business enemy of EARNSHAW. His son J. R. Arnold, who was apprenticed to BREGUET, continued the business and went into partnership with E. J. Dent, who later made 'BIG BEN'.

Artificial Clock   Early name for a mechanical clock to differentiate it from a natural 'clock' such as the sun or moon.

Ashmolean Museum Collection   This is at Oxford and includes fine examples of early watches (including the REPEATER invented by Daniel Quare), clocks, and the earliest ASTROLABE known.

Astrolabe   Elaborate ALTITUDE DIAL for finding the time in TEMPORAL or EQUAL HOURS, probably invented by the Greeks.

Astronaut's Clock   Extremely accurate timekeeper that is unaffected by fierce acceleration and varying gravity for space travel. Among those so far developed are the SATELLITE TIMER, QUARTZ CLOCK, and the EARTH PATH INDICATOR. For ground control systems, QUARTZ and particularly ATOMIC CLOCKS are suitable. *See* **Time.**

Astronomer Royal   First appointed for FINDING THE LONGITUDE by astronomical observation. Responsible today also for TIME DETERMINATION and TIME DISTRIBUTION. John FLAMSTEED was the first. Of others, Bradley discovered NUTATION, set up the TIME BALL, and started a time distribution service, AIRY improved clock accuracy. Dyson adopted the FREE PENDULUM, and Spencer-Jones adopted the QUARTZ CLOCK. *See* **Greenwich Observatory.** There are separate Astronomers Royal for England (Herstmonceux), for Scotland (Edinburgh), and Northern Ireland (Armagh), Australia, and South Africa.

Astronomer's Pendulum Early astronomers used a weight which swung on a cord to measure time, before the PENDULUM CLOCK was invented. The time of swing was calculated by GALILEO and HUYGENS. *See* **Observatory Clock.**

Astronomical Clock Clock with astronomical indications, such as SIDEREAL time and the movements of the Earth, Moon, and planets, on dials or by models. Earliest mechanical clocks were astronomical. Famous makers were DONDI, who designed the first of all, BURGI, BALDEWIN, HABRECHT, RAINGO, and JANVIER. *See also* **Globe Clock, Orrery** *and* **Strasbourg Clock.** The latest large astronomical clocks made in England are one in York Cathedral, another in the *Financial Times* building in Cannon Street, London, E.C.4, and a replica of DONDI's CLOCK.

Astronomical Ephemeris Tables which include EQUATION OF TIME figures. Since 1960, published jointly by the Royal GREENWICH OBSERVATORY and the United States Naval Observatory. Incorporates the original NAUTICAL ALMANAC and the American Nautical Almanac.

Atmos Clock Automatically-wound Swiss table clock. An aneroid bellows is pressed out by a rise in temperature to operate a mechanism that winds the mainspring. Has a TORSION PENDULUM.

Atomic Clock The radio frequencies emitted by atoms and molecules at low pressures are fixed and unchanging with time. They can therefore be used to control a radio oscillator itself controlling a QUARTZ CLOCK. The most accurate atomic clock or frequency standard ever made employs as its 'pendulum' the vibration of the caesium atom, which is at 9,192,631,770 cycles a second. It was developed by Louis Essen and J. V. L. Parry at the NATIONAL PHYSICAL LABORATORY. Their first model, C.1, of

1955, for checking the quartz clocks at the laboratory and the Post Office standard frequency broadcasts from the Rugby Radio station, was the world's first atomic clock to go into service. *See* **Radio Time Signal.** The latest version, C.3, is accurate to the equivalent of one second in 3,000 years and has shown that the Earth's rotation is slowing down by about two MILLISECONDS a year after making other corrections for PRECESSION OF THE EQUINOX and NUTATION. *See* **Ammonia Maser.**

Atomic Time   An ATOMIC CLOCK, using as its standard of frequency the vibrations of atoms of the element caesium, is much more accurate than any other time standard, such as the Earth, and the QUARTZ CLOCK. Therefore Atomic Time will probably replace EPHEMERIS TIME. A network was set up in 1961 using atomic clocks in the U.K. and U.S.A. to provide time signals accurate to half a MILLISECOND over a large part of the Earth's surface for checking artificial satellites, etc.

Automatic Clock Winding   System used on many new TOWER CLOCKS, in which an electric motor is automatically switched on and off to wind up the weight every quarter of an hour or so. Many old tower clocks are being converted from hand winding, which took an hour or more daily. A Huygens ENDLESS CHAIN is used which provides MAINTAINING POWER. Automatic winding is employed in most domestic BATTERY CLOCKS, an electro-magnet rewinding a small mainspring every few minutes. The arrangement for driving ELECTRIC MASTER CLOCKS is also a form of automatic winding. *See* **Atmos Clock** *and* **Light Clock.**

Automaton   Animated mechanical figure or scene. Earliest were Egyptian, followed by Greek and Roman gods which pointed to 'chosen' kings or leaders. Some were worked by

16

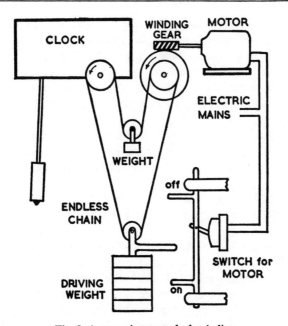

Fig. 2. Automatic tower clock winding.

water, like the displays on su sung's clock, and the large and elaborate scenes still existing at Heilbronn. Early automata worked by mechanical clocks were called JACKS. Later, jousting-knights, waterfalls, windmills, ships at sea, animals playing musical instruments, acrobats, etc., were worked by the clock-work and often associated with MUSICAL CLOCKS. A famous one was Bridge's Microcosm (now in the British Museum). James Cox was a renowned maker in the eighteenth century. Watches were also made with automata (occasionally of erotic scenes which were concealed until operated by a secret PUSH PIECE). One of the most recent large clocks with automaton is the GUINNESS CLOCK. The word 'automation' is derived from this (Plate 8).

17

Auxiliary Compensation Additional form of temperature compensator for a COMPENSATION BALANCE in order to avoid MIDDLE TEMPERATURE ERROR. A great variety of such compensations were invented in the nineteenth century. Best solutions were the GUILLAUME, DITISHEIM, and OVALIZING BALANCES for MARINE CHRONOMETERS and high-grade watches.

Babylonian Hours Early system of time reckoning in Babylon. A day and night period was divided into a continuous series of 1 to 24 EQUAL HOURS, but they started at sunrise each day.

Baillie, G. H. (1883–1951) Historian who specialized in clocks and watches and compiled a list of 36,000 makers.

Bain Clock One of the earliest electric clocks. Some, like grandfather clocks in appearance, still exist and work off ground batteries—coke and zinc buried in the ground—which require watering in dry weather. There is one in the BRITISH HOROLOGICAL INSTITUTE Museum. Alexander Bain, a Scot from Thurso, also invented SLAVE DIALS.

Balance A controlling device for clocks and watches which, through the ESCAPEMENT, momentarily unlocks and re-locks the gears at short intervals to move the hands. IMPULSES from the escapement keep the balance swinging to and fro. The first was the FOLIOT, a bar with weights on the ends used on large clocks in the thirteenth century. In the fourteenth century for watches and smaller clocks, this became the DUMBELL and the BALANCE WHEEL.

Balance Wheel A BALANCE for clocks or watches which is shaped like a wheel. The earliest were made of steel or brass and had one spoke, the swing sometimes being limited by the spoke knocking against a steel pin or a HOG'S BRISTLE. Balance wheels with two spokes (an arm) soon became universal. The HAIR-

18

SPRING was added in the seventeenth century and the increasing timekeeping accuracy stimulated attempts at TEMPERATURE COMPENSATION, resulting in various forms of CUT BALANCE, often with AUXILIARY COMPENSATION. The invention of ELINVAR for the hairspring caused a return to the plain balance wheel made of beryllium alloy or nickel for almost all clocks and watches, but MARINE CHRONOMETERS still have cut balances except for one made in the U.S.A. which has an OVALIZING BALANCE. Most modern balance wheels have a fifth of a second BEAT (Fig. 5).

Balance and Spring A BALANCE WHEEL combined with a spiral or cylindrical HAIRSPRING, which is the oscillating time standard in almost every watch and very large numbers of clocks. The two have to be considered together for purposes of TEMPERATURE COMPENSATION, REGULATION, etc.

Balance Cock The COCK that holds the bearing, normally a SHOCK ABSORBER, for one end of the BALANCE.

Balance Spring Alternative name for the HAIRSPRING.

Balance Staff The shaft or axle of the BALANCE.

Ball Clock This has three meanings. 1. A clock with a ball-shaped case. Many versions have appeared from the eighteenth century to the present day. In some the ball has a REVOLVING BAND showing the hour and on others there is a normal dial with curved hands. One of the latter form made in quantity from about 1875 to 1925 had a sphere on the head of a bust of Atlas with a cupid on each side. Also FALLING BALL CLOCK. 2. A clock in which the driving power is provided by a heavy steel ball or balls moving down a, usually spiral, track. The balls are raised to the top of the track by a clockwork mechanism. The idea was to provide more even power than springs give and make the clock more compact than a weight-driven one. It was employed by Nicholas Radeloff, a pupil of BURGI in the seventeenth century (Plate 3). 3. A rolling ball clock in which a ball running along a track is the timekeeping standard, instead of a PENDULUM or BALANCE. Developed particularly by GROLLIER and CONGREVE (Plate 6). *See* **Congreve Clock** *and* **Tower of Babel Clock.**

Ball Watch   Small modern ball-shaped watch, with the dial at the bottom, hung from a necklace or brooch. Reminiscent of the very first MUSK BALL WATCHES. *See* **Watch.**

Balloon Clock   Style of wooden case for a spring-driven clock, introduced about 1760. From the front it has roughly the outline of a Montgolfier balloon.

Fig. 3. Balloon clock.

Band   Watch strap or BRACELET. *See also* **Expanding Bracelet.**

Banjo Clock   The case is similar to a banjo in shape. Invented by Simon Willard, U.S.A., about 1800, made in large numbers and particularly favoured by the railway companies as station timekeepers (and status symbols—the more important the station, the bigger the banjo).

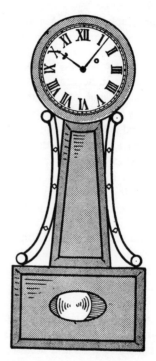

Fig. 4. Banjo clock.

Banking Pin   A pin or stop to prevent excessive motion of a BALANCE, HAIRSPRING, the lever of a LEVER ESCAPEMENT, a PENDULUM, GRAVITY ARM, etc. *See* **Bristle Regulator.**

Bar Movement   Early form of partly machine-made watch MOVEMENT in which bars, or BRIDGES and COCKS, are used to hold bearings for one PIVOT of each wheel, for easy dismantling.

Barlow, Edward (1636–1716) Clergyman who changed his name from Booth and became famous as a clockmaker by inventing RACK STRIKING, a form of REPEATING work for clocks and watches, and also (with TOMPION and Wm. Houghton) an early form of the CYLINDER ESCAPEMENT.

Barograph Clock A modern form of DRUM CLOCK used to drive the chart in a barograph.

Barometric Error Changes in RATE caused by varying air pressure; in accurate pendulum clocks to the extent of ¾ sec. a day per inch of mercury. Compensators worked by mercury and by aneroid barometers have been invented, but the modern method is to keep the pendulum in low-pressure air in a sealed chamber and to keep the air pressure and temperature constant. To reduce the error in free air, the pendulum BOB should be a cylinder as wide as it is high of the densest possible material, according to Colin Frye (1956). Few are, however. Watches are also affected. One modern wrist-watch is in a vacuum case.

Barrel Drum-shaped container of watch or clock MAINSPRING. A GOING BARREL has teeth around it and drives the wheels (Plate 2). A spring barrel in conjunction with a FUSEE has no teeth and drives by winding a chain or gut line round itself. The drum round which the gut, rope or chain of a weight-driven clock is wound is also a barrel. So is the drum carrying pins or cams to operate hammers striking bells or a musical comb in MUSICAL CLOCKS and BOXES.

Basket Top Pierced ornamental metalwork forming the domed top of a BRACKET CLOCK.

Bath Clock Fine LONG CASE CLOCK in the Grand Pump Room at Bath, Somerset, given in 1709 by TOMPION. It is 9 ft. high in an oak case and also shows the EQUATION OF TIME. A sundial was supplied with it to check it, but has been lost.

Baton   A stroke used on a dial instead of a number.

Battery Clock   Mechanical clock with a special AUTOMATIC WINDING arrangement operated every few minutes by a torch battery which lasts for about a year. In one form, a small Swiss PRECISION CLOCK, however, the battery drives a continuously running electric motor driving a REMONTOIRE. Also a pendulum clock operated by a battery. *See* **Eureka Clock, Bulle Clock, Electronic Clock, Thousand Day Clock.**

Battery Watch   An ELECTRIC or ELECTRONIC WATCH powered by a tiny battery, which lasts over a year. The Mallory battery is about $\frac{1}{2}$ in. diameter and $\frac{1}{8}$ in. thick. It has capacity of 80 milliamp-hours at 1.3 volts. An atomic battery for watches about the same size with lead screening to last about five years has been developed, and another Mallory battery of 140 milliamp-hours.

Beat   Watchmaker's name for 'tick'. A grandfather clock 'beats seconds' and a man's wrist-watch beats fifths of a second. Smaller watches are usually made to beat faster. Cheaper ones often beat slower. *See* **Dead Beat.**

Beat Plate   Another name for a DEGREE PLATE.

Beauvais Cathedral Clock   Large ASTRONOMICAL CLOCK with AUTOMATA, built in Beauvais, France, from 1857–66.

Bedpost Frame   Style of TOWER CLOCK made in the late eighteenth and nineteenth centuries with corner posts to the frame like Victorian bedposts with large knobs.

Bell Top   Top of a BRACKET CLOCK shaped like a church bell with concave sides (but rectangular, looking down on it).

23

Bench Key Star-shaped clock key with ends to fit different WINDING SQUARES. Also key with adjustable end.

Berne Clock Early public clock with AUTOMATA in a tower in Berne, Switzerland.

Berthoud, Ferdinand (1729–1807) Swiss maker of very fine watches, clocks, and MARINE CHRONOMETERS, who was to have entered the Church but became a watchmaker in Paris at the age of 16. Invented a DETENT ESCAPEMENT, and wrote many technical papers. His nephew Louis Berthoud (1750–1813) also became famous for his chronometers.

Bezel The rim, usually of metal, that holds the glass of a watch or clock.

Big Ben Name given to the WESTMINSTER PALACE CLOCK, but actually the 13½ ton bell on which it strikes the hours. The bell was cast in Whitechapel and hauled to Westminster on a trolley drawn by 16 horses. It was named after Sir Benjamin Hall, a large man who was Chief Commissioner in 1859. The first bell made weighed 14 tons and cracked badly when it was struck by its 8 cwt. hammer. When the present bell was hauled into place and struck, despite warnings by the clock designer Lord GRIMTHORPE to the architect that the structure was too weak, the vibrations thoroughly frightened everyone present and the mountings had to be strengthened immediately. The second Big Ben also cracked soon after it was installed, so the hour was struck on the next biggest bell, and Big Ben was not used for three years until 1862. Then it was given an eighth turn and has sounded ever since despite the crack. It can be heard four miles away. The B.B.C. first broadcast the sound of Big Ben on 31 December 1923, and soon after fixed a permanent microphone in the tower. The present hammer weighs 4 cwt. Striking can be controlled by hand and when the Monarch dies, his or her age is struck on 'Big Ben'. *See* **Westminster Chimes.**

Biggest Clock The world's largest clock dial, 50 ft. across, is on the Colgate-Palmolive plant in Jersey City, U.S.A. (1924). The minute hand is 27 ft. 3 in. long. Britain's largest is the Singer Sewing Machine factory clock, Clydebank, Scotland, with four dials each 26 ft. across and minute hands 12 ft. 9 in. long.

Billiards Clock Form of TIME SWITCH operated by the insertion of a coin so that it turns off the lights over a billiards table (or operates a mechanism to trap the balls in bar billiards) after a given time.

Bi-Metallic Made of two different metals, each of which has a different rate of expansion when warmed. A bi-metallic strip of steel and brass riveted together, bends when heated or cooled. It was invented by HARRISON in the eighteenth century for his COMPENSATION CURB, and is today used in millions for thermostats. The bi-metallic BALANCE WHEEL rim was developed by EARNSHAW. All bi-metallic balances except the OVALISING one are CUT BALANCES.

Bi-Metallic Balance A COMPENSATION BALANCE made of steel and brass strip joined together so that they bend when heated to give TEMPERATURE COMPENSATION. Almost always a CUT BALANCE. On early timekeepers the strips were riveted together. EARNSHAW invented the method still used of fusing molten brass on to a steel disc and cutting the balance wheel from this. *See illustration overleaf.*

Bird Cage Clock A cage with SINGING BIRDS in it which also has a clock dial on the bottom so that it can be seen when the cage is suspended. Made around 1780, probably of French and Swiss parts.

Bird Cage Frame Spindly box-like frame of TOWER CLOCKS

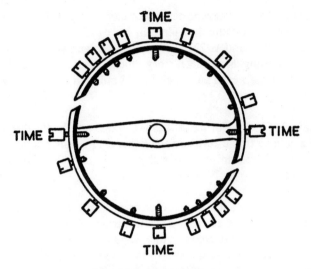

Fig. 5. Bi-metallic balance.

after about 1515. From about 1380–1515, these wrought-iron frames were massive, with corner standards like church buttresses. *See* **Bedpost Frame.**

Black Forest Clock   Type of clock made entirely of wood with VERGE and FOLIOT, and one hand. Strikes on a glass bell. First made there about 1680 by a carpenter Lorenz Frey of Spurzen St Margen, who copied a sample. Now, any clock from this area of Germany.

Blacksmith's Clock   The earliest big clocks were often made by blacksmiths, parts being forged and fire welded. Thos. TOMPION started his working life as a blacksmith.

Blacksmiths Company   Before the CLOCKMAKERS COMPANY was formed, the Worshipful Company of Blacksmiths had a monopoly of clockmaking. This led later to a strong feud between the two, long since settled.

Blind Man's Watch   Pocket or wrist-watch with knobs at the hours and sometimes a double one at 12, which can be opened so that the hand or hands can be felt. *See* **Tact Watch.** Modern versions include ALARM WATCHES (Plate 8).

Blinking Eye Clock   Another name for MOVING EYE CLOCK.

Bob   Weight on the end of a PENDULUM. Early BOB PENDULUMS had pear-shaped weights of brass. Others are usually cylindrical, or lenticular, i.e. disc shaped, and of brass, cast iron, lead encased in brass, zinc, or jars of mercury in the MERCURIAL PENDULUM. The RATE is unaffected by the weight of the bob, but *see* **Barometric Error.** Occasionally a novelty bob such as a model of a child on a swing or a fish on a line is used. In others the clock itself is the pendulum bob.

Bob Pendulum   The earliest form of PENDULUM, with a pear-shaped brass weight (the bob) on the threaded end of a wire rod. The bob has a core of pear wood in which the wire formed a thread for adjustment of length.

Fig. 6. Bob pendulum.

Bolt and Shutter   A form of MAINTAINING POWER used on some fine quality LONG CASE CLOCKS. The winding hole is normally covered by a shutter; moving this aside by means of a lever in order to insert the KEY, applies power to the clock during winding so that its timekeeping is unaffected.

Bookmaker's Clock Bag   Special bag with a time lock used for betting slips collected by bookmaker's runners. The runner closes the bag which then locks and starts a watch in the lock. The jaws of the bag have 'teeth' which prevent slips being squeezed in after locking. The bookmaker can open the bag with a special key and note the time which has elapsed since it was closed.

Boulle Clock   Clock with a case of tortoiseshell inlaid with metal or ivory, or this inlaid with tortoiseshell. Perfected by Charles André Boulle (1642–1732). Also called 'Buhl'.

'Bounty' Watch   Duplicate of John HARRISON's famous No. 4 watch made in 1772 by Larcum KENDALL and also known as 'K2'. It was loaned to Captain Bligh in 1787 for navigation of H.M.S. *Bounty* and taken by Fletcher Christian, leader of the mutineers, when Bligh was set adrift in an open boat. After the mutineers went to Pitcairn Island, Fletcher Christian sold it to a Captain Folger of the American whaler *Topaz* (some say to secure his passage from Pitcairn Island, for he disappeared afterwards). Folger was robbed of the watch by Spaniards at the 'Robinson Crusoe' island of Juan Fernandez. Somehow it reached a muleteer in Chile and passed through other hands until Captain Herbert of H.M.S. *Calliope* acquired it and brought it to England in 1843. It now belongs to the Royal United Service Institution, London.

Box Chronometer   A MARINE CHRONOMETER fixed in gimbals in a special box so that it will remain level. Some modern ones, and surveyors' chronometers, however, do not have gimbal fittings in the box.

Bracelet Watch band or STRAP. Metal ones are usually of gold or are ROLLED GOLD, GOLD PLATED, STAINLESS STEEL or a combination of them. Most are FLEXIBLE WATCH BANDS. Some are EXPANDING. Elaborate bracelets for ladies' watches are set with all kinds of gem stones and are classed among the finest jewellery.

Bracket Clock Normal name for a wooden-cased clock commonly made in the seventeenth and eighteenth centuries for standing on a wall bracket or table. Usually fairly large and always portable, having a handle on the top. Often of ebony veneer with gilt metal ornaments. A more correct name would be 'table clock' or 'mantel clock' (Plate 1).

Braille Watch A BLIND MAN'S WATCH. *See also* **Tact Watch.**

Brass Alloy of copper and zinc introduced into clockmaking in the sixteenth century on the Continent of Europe, and adopted in England at the beginning of the seventeenth century. First used for cases and dials and later for PLATES, and WHEELS (early in the seventeenth century). ARBORS, PINIONS, and levers continued to be of iron or steel. The clockmaker cast his own brass and hardened it by hammering it. Brass and steel are still used, the brass being rolled and sometimes 'prinked' (like a lawn) to give extra hardness.

Break Arch Shape of the top of clock cases or dials where the straight edge is broken by an arch which does not extend to the full width. *See* **Arch Dial.**

Breguet, A. L. (1747–1823) Considered by some the greatest watchmaker of all time, he was a Swiss who was taught at the Versailles watchmaking school (which was started by an Englishman). He then spent some years as a journeyman watchmaker, probably in London, setting up on his own in

Paris in 1775 when he was immediately successful. His watches included PERPETUALS, which were and are highly prized, and SUBSCRIPTION. He invented a SHOCK ABSORBER known as the 'parachute' and the TOURBILLON. Many forgers tried to imitate Breguet's watches, so he used a SECRET SIGNATURE. During the French Revolution, he fled from his business at Quai de l'Horloge on the Seine, Paris, to Le Locle, Switzerland, but he returned later. His work was of superb quality. *See* **Marie Antoinette Watch** *and* **Oil.**

Breguet Spring An ordinary HAIRSPRING, whether spiral or CYLINDRICAL, moves out of centre as it opens and closes with the swinging of the BALANCE. This affects timekeeping as the spring is not ISOCHRONOUS. Isochronism can be greatly improved by curving the ends of a cylindrical spring in a special way towards the centre; ARNOLD patented various curves in 1782. BREGUET discovered in about 1800 that the same effect could be obtained with a spiral spring by giving the outer coil an upward kink and curving it so that it was fixed near the centre of the balance. *See* **Overcoil.** It is somewhat difficult to use a REGULATOR on hairsprings with a 'Breguet overcoil' so they are usually FREE SPRUNG. The mathematical theory of terminal curves was later worked out by PHILLIPS and Lossier.

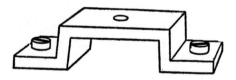

Fig. 7. Bridge.

Bridge A metal bar which carries one or more PIVOT bearings and is fixed at both ends.

Bristle Regulator Before the HAIRSPRING was invented, the swing of the plain BALANCE was often limited in the sixteenth century by two stiff hog's bristles, which projected in the path of the arm of the balance and could be moved in and out from the centre to regulate the clock or watch. *See* **Banking.**

British Horological Industry In 1368, King Edward III invited three Dutch 'orologiers' to England to start clockmaking. During the seventeenth and eighteenth centuries under control of the CLOCKMAKERS COMPANY, it became the world's biggest, employing 70,000 craftsmen, who invented nearly all improvements to timekeeping so that even today no mechanical clock or watch is made anywhere in the world without a British invention in it. *See* **Tompion, Graham, Harrison, Mudge, Barlow, Arnold, Earnshaw, Grimthorpe.** The ENGLISH LEVER became the most desired watch of all. In the nineteenth century, Craftmakers in PRESCOT, COVENTRY and CLERKENWELL refused to accept changes brought about by factory manufacture and in a few years the industry was dead. Clockmaking continued, but was badly damaged when Hitler heavily subsidized the German industry in order to destroy the French and British industries, upon which fuse-making depended, but MARINE CHRONOMETERS continued to be made. After the Second World War, the Government, having learned its lesson, re-established the watchmaking industry and encouraged clock manufacture, both on the most modern lines. Production now runs at about eight and a half million clocks and three million watches yearly. The main watchmaking centres are at Ystradgynlais, in South Wales; Cheltenham, Gloucestershire; and Scotland. All mechanical alarm clocks are made in three Scottish factories. Clocks are made around the London area and elsewhere, and industrial clocks of every possible type come from all parts of the country. TOWER CLOCKS are made in London, Middlesex, Derby, Leeds, Edinburgh, etc. There are still one or two makers by hand, and many ELECTRIC CLOCK makers.

British Horological Institute   Formed in 1858 to develop the science of horology and encourage high craftsmanship. Today it runs correspondence courses in technical horology, conducts national examinations, awards qualifications, controls apprenticeship, registers qualified repairers, runs exhibitions, and advises on national matters. Its President is the Astronomer Royal. At its headquarters in 35 Northampton Square, Clerkenwell, London, E.C.1, is a museum and the ILBERT LIBRARY. Its monthly *Horological Journal* is the world's oldest trade and technical journal. For their own protection, members of the public should deal only with B.H.I. REGISTERED CRAFTSMEN and retailers.

British Museum Collection   Includes the ILBERT COLLECTION, making it the world's most important, of 325 clocks and 1,360 watches and their movements, representing almost every invention or improvement in timekeeping, as well as artistic merit. Included are the Strasbourg tower clock of 1589; a table clock of 1580 by Bart. Newsum, clockmaker to Queen Elizabeth I; Thos. TOMPION's clock for GREENWICH OBSERVATORY; a magnificent MUSICAL CLOCK by Nicholas Vallin of London, 1598; one of the first LONG CASE CLOCKS, by A. FROMANTEEL; the 'Mulberry Tompion'; the original CONGREVE CLOCK; REGULATORS by GRAHAM and MUDGE: Mudge's first MARINE CHRONOMETER, and his first LEVER ESCAPEMENT clock; and many very interesting watches from the sixteenth to nineteenth century including fine ENAMELLED ones and examples by BREGUET.

'Britten'   Casual name for a standard book on old clocks and watches first published in 1899 and written by F. J. Britten (d. 1913), secretary of the BRITISH HOROLOGICAL INSTITUTE for 33 years.

British Summer Time   GREENWICH MEAN TIME advanced by an hour in the U.K. during the summer, the dates being fixed by a Parliamentary Order yearly. *See* **Daylight Saving.**

Brocot Clock   A French clock with a PIN PALLET escapement of ANCHOR form combined with a pendulum invented by A. Brocot (d. 1878). Usually this escapement, with its semi-circular agate PALLETS, is visible on the front of the dial and the clock case is of marble.

Buhl Clock   *See* **Boulle Clock.**

Bull, Randolph   One of the earliest English watchmakers. The BRITISH MUSEUM has a watch of his dated 1590.

Bulle Clock   Early BATTERY CLOCK invented by Favre-Bulle. The pendulum BOB is a coil of wire which swings over a fixed, curved, permanent magnet. A switch operated by the pendulum sends a current of electricity through the coil during a swing, making it an electro-magnet and thus IMPULSING it. The pendulum drives the hands by a pawl and ratchet mechanism.

Bull's-eye Glass   The thick centre 'bull's-eye' of old crown glass, cut circular and used in the door of a LONG CASE CLOCK, to show that the pendulum was swinging. Most pendulum apertures were round or oval windows of ordinary glass.

Burgi, Jobst (1552–1632)   Master clockmaker of Swiss origin, apprenticed to HABRECHT, and working at the Court of Kassel in a team with the astronomers Tycho Brahe, Kepler, and others. Inventor of the CROSS BEAT ESCAPEMENT. Several fine GLOBE CLOCKS by him exist in museums in Kassel, Vienna, the Louvre, Paris, and Gotha.

Calendar Many centuries ago, Emperors employed astronomers to fix their own calendars. Julius Caesar carried out a drastic reform, resulting in our present calendar, because officials were altering dates to suit themselves. Augustus Caesar changed leap year to every four years instead of three and the name of the month Sextilis to Augustus (August). Pope Gregory made the final change by introducing 97 leap years in 400 years instead of 100. The Gregorian calendar was accepted by Catholic countries in 1582. England did not come into line until 170 years later, thinking this a Popish plot.

Calendar Reform The present calendar wastes time and money because of the varying lengths of months and different days on which festivals occur. The League of Nations proposed a reform and so has United Nations. Neither has been accepted. The U.N. World Calendar gives 26 working days in each month and 91 in each quarter. Days of months would always fall on the same dates. This leaves an odd day at the end of the year without a number to be called World Day (or New Year's Day). Leap Year's Day would fall similarly between 30 June and 1 July, and be unnumbered.

Calendar Clock One showing the date, sometimes the month, and even the day of the week. Most have to be corrected at the end of months of less than 31 days. Self-correcting versions are called PERPETUAL CALENDARS. A pin on a wheel turning once in 24 hours operates the mechanism around midnight.

Calendar Watch Wrist- or pocket watch showing the date through an aperture in the dial. On some the date can be reset by moving the minute hand back and forth across 12 o'clock (midnight). On others the hands have to be twirled through 24 hours to move each date.

Calotte Travelling clock which folds into leather case or portfolio. 'Calotte' actually refers to the circular metal case of the clock itself.

34

Camera Timer Special clock with DIGITAL RECORDING built into cameras used for aerial surveys, etc. Each picture then gives on the edge a miniature record of the time at which it was taken. Camera timers of a different design are made for horse racing, athletics, and other sporting events, to give 'photo-finishes'. The camera faces along the winning line. The film moves past a slit, which acts as the camera aperture, the speed being appropriate to the speed of the contestants. Thus the camera records a series of events on one film. It also shows, on the edge, the timing of the competitors; the timer is set going by a starting gate or breaking of a light ray, at the beginning of the race.

Candle Clock Candle with bands marked on it to indicate passing time, said to have been invented by King Arthur.

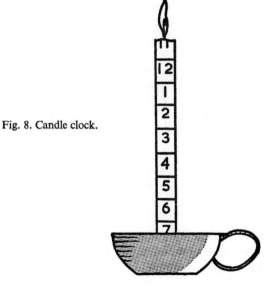

Fig. 8. Candle clock.

Canonical Hours Seven periods known as Matins, Prime, Tierce, Sext, Nones, Vespers, and Compline into which early monasteries divided the day, to control working and prayer times. Froissart, in his *Chronicles*, refers to Canonical Hours before 1377 and a.m. and p.m. after that date.

Canterbury Cathedral Clock There is a record of the first clock being erected here in 1292, four years after the first WESTMINSTER PALACE CLOCK may have been erected.

Cap Separate dustproof cover inside the case to cover a watch MOVEMENT, common from about 1750. Superseded by the Borgel screwed-up case and others more dustproof up to today's WATERPROOF CASE.

Captain Cook's Watches This famous sailor tested many of the earliest timekeepers for FINDING THE LONGITUDE including those made by HARRISON, MUDGE, ARNOLD, and KENDALL.

Captain Scott's Watch A DECK WATCH by S. Smith and Sons recovered from Captain Scott's body in the Antarctic and used again by Dr Fuchs on the Trans-Antarctic Expedition in 1957. Stolen at London Airport in 1961.

Carriage Clock Smallish portable clock, spring-driven with BALANCE. The earliest are like very large pocket watches (Plate 7). French ones have a rectangular brass case usually with glass sides and top, and with a handle on top; each has a PLATFORM ESCAPEMENT, often strikes, sometimes chimes, or is a REPEATER. *See* **Sedan Clock.**

Cartel Clock Ornate French wall clock in cast bronze or carved wood with a gilt finish and half-seconds PENDULUM, of Louis XV period.

36

Case, Clock   The earliest clocks known had no cases, but soon metal panels were used between vertical corner posts to keep out dust, as in the LANTERN CLOCK. Even today TURRET CLOCKS rarely have protective cases. Decorative cases go back four centuries when elaborate engraving, repoussé and carving on brass or precious metals, and rock crystal were employed. Almost every material available has since been used, from reinforced concrete to cardboard. Today most common materials are wood, brass, ceramics and plastics for domestic clocks of which current designs have developed from GOTHIC, LANTERN and BRACKET CLOCKS.

Case, Watch   Earliest watch cases were ball shaped (wrongly called NUREMBERG EGGS) and made of gilded brass. Gilded bronze was common in the sixteenth century. The ball was rapidly superseded by the DRUM shape which became rounded at the edges after about 1575, when octagonal shapes also appeared. Oval shapes were introduced just before 1600 (*see* **Puritan Watch**). There were no glasses and the single hand was read through the pierced decoration of the cover, although rock crystal was sometimes used as a 'glass'. The case was hinged below the PENDANT, the MOVEMENT being hinged on the same line, but held in the bottom of the case by a small catch. The PAIR CASE increased in popularity after mid-seventeenth century (*see* **Cap**). Considerable decoration was applied from this time, of rock crystal, ENAMEL, chasing, chiselling, and REPOUSSÉ. The FORM WATCH also appeared. Gold, silver, brass, and PINCHBECK were used and outer pair cases were sometimes of leather (*see* **Pinwork**), SHAGREEN, or PIQUÉ. Modern wrist-watch cases are of gold alloy, stainless steel, or (for cheap ones) aluminium alloy. They are machined from solid shaped bar, or formed from sheet by press tools by specialist manufacturers. The fine finish on gold is obtained by diamond tools. Modern cases are three-piece, two-piece, or one-piece (which is 'opened' by removing the UNBREAKABLE GLASS). *See* **Waterproof Case.**

Cassiobury Clock A TURRET CLOCK from Cassiobury Park, Hertfordshire, still with FOLIOT made about 1600.

Centre of Oscillation The time of swing of a PENDULUM depends on its length (only) from the centre of SUSPENSION to the centre of oscillation, which is also called the 'centre of percussion'. The latter is an imaginary point within the BOB related to the centre of gravity. This explains why adding a weight above the bob makes the clock go faster; it raises the centre of oscillation and makes the pendulum 'shorter'.

Centre Seconds Hand Seconds hand of a watch or clock pivoted in the centre of the dial. Also called 'sweep seconds'.

Certificate *See* **Rating Certificate, Kew 'A' Certificate** *and* **Craftsmanship Test.**

Chamber Clock Earliest form of domestic clock. Made of iron by blacksmiths like the first TOWER CLOCKS. Driven by weights and hung on a wall in the hall which was the centre of the medieval home, so that its striking could be heard all round. Also called a 'house clock' (Plate 5). *See* **Lantern Clock.**

Chapter Ring The circle on which the hours are marked. On antique clocks this is often a separate brass ring engraved with the numerals, etc., the engraving being filled with black wax, and the ring SILVERED and LACQUERED.

Chapters The hour marks of a clock.

Chatelaine Watch Watch with an ornamental, and often enamelled, chain with trinkets attached. A true chatelaine was the chain holding the keys, worn by the mistress of the medieval castle; it became popular again in Victorian times as an ornament.

Chelsea Clock   Another name for SHIP'S BELL CLOCK, as many are made by the Chelsea Clock Co., U.S.A.

Chemical Clock   Device using chemical cartridges for timing periods of electric current flow. The current 'eats up' the cartridge, the reduced length showing the time on a scale.

Chess Clock   Special TIMER for chess players with two MOVE-MENTS and two dials, one showing the accumulating time occupied by one player in his moves, and the other the time of the other player. As each player makes a move, he presses a knob on the clock which stops the hands of his dial and starts those of his opponent's dial.

Chime   Simple melody on bells or gongs at the quarter or half hours and preceding the hour. The earliest was the TING TANG on two bells. Most are on four bells, but there are others on any number. The WESTMINSTER CHIME is a four-bell. Notre Dame in Paris is an eight-bell. The Whittington chime of Bow Church, London, is on eleven bells, but is sometimes modified so that it can be played on fewer.

Chiming Clock   Clock that CHIMES. TOWER CLOCKS and some antique clocks chime on bells. Modern domestic clocks usually have the WESTMINSTER or modified Whittington chime on rod GONGS. The hour note is produced by hitting several gongs simultaneously. A turning chime BARREL with pins or cams operates GONG HAMMERS to produce the tune. In such clocks there are three separate MAINSPRINGS or BARRELS and trains of wheels for timekeeping, striking, and chiming.

Chinese Clocks   The Chinese produced the transitional clock between the old inaccurate WATER CLOCK and the mechanical clock. A monk I-Hsing probably invented the first ESCAPEMENT in A.D. 725. The Chinese had no part in the development of the mechanical clock, but the present régime has introduced clock and watchmaking industries. Many clocks (and watches) of special design were made in the eighteenth and nineteenth centuries by English and Swiss makers for the Chinese market. *See* **Su Sung's Clock.**

Chinese Duplex   Swiss watch with a special kind of DUPLEX escapement made for the Chinese market in mid-nineteenth century. This made the CENTRE SECONDS HAND appear to be DEAD BEAT, and move every second. Such watches were usually made in pairs. The MOVEMENTS had elaborately engraved and scalloped-edged BRIDGES, which could be seen through an inside glass cover.

Chippendale Case   Clock case based on the designs of Thos. Chippendale in his book of furniture designs, 1754. Usually in mahogany.

Chronograph   A timepiece that can be started and stopped to measure short time intervals. Usually a watch for timing only is called a TIMER or STOPWATCH and one that shows the time of day as well is called a 'chronograph'. Wrist chronographs often have special scales such as TELEMETER and TACHYMETER. There are also chronographs for technical and scientific uses. The recording chronograph was invented in 1807 by Thomas Young, who used a revolving drum on which a pencil marked the beginning and end of the time interval. The electro-magnetic chronograph was invented by Wheatstone, or the younger BREGUET. Washington Observatory was the first to use a chronograph for measuring star transits in 1849. *See* **Transit Instrument.** Chronographs for very short time intervals are sometimes electronic and to confuse the name still more, the makers called them CHRONOMETERS.

Chronographer (or chronopher)   Apparatus controlled by a clockwork CONICAL PENDULUM used from 1852 by the Electric Telegraph Co., railway companies, and the General Post Office, to send TIME SIGNALS from GREENWICH OBSERVATORY by wire to some 1,000 towns and to railway stations. Work at telegraph offices was stopped a few minutes before 10 a.m. and before 1 p.m. to receive the 'time current', which moved the telegraph (galvanometer) needles to one side, then flicked them to the other exactly at the hour. 'BIG BEN's' timekeeping was originally checked by chronographer.

Chronometer   Originally a name for a metronome, but applied to a precision timekeeper in 1714 by Jeremy Thacker. Now a general name for a non-pendulum precision clock or a watch, although purists insist that it means a timepiece with a DETENT ESCAPEMENT, such as the MARINE CHRONOMETER. Makers of electronic instruments call their timekeeping devices ELECTRONIC CHRONOMETERS. The Admiralty names high precision LEVER WATCHES 'chronometers'. In Switzerland since 1951, no manufacturer has been allowed to call a watch a 'chronometer' unless it has obtained an official RATING CERTIFICATE from one of the testing bureaux.

Chronometer Escapement   Another name for the DETENT ESCAPEMENT.

Chronoscope   Name usually given to a continuously running timepiece for recording short time intervals by engaging and disengaging a hand. Invented in 1840 by Wheatstone, whose instrument was accurate to 1/60th sec. HIPP made one a few years later accurate to 1/1,000th sec. Today the very much more accurate QUARTZ CRYSTAL CLOCK, AMMONIA MASER, or ATOMIC CLOCK is used. *See* **Timer.**

Church Clock   The oldest clocks in England are usually in the towers of cathedrals and churches, although some were placed in the church itself. On the Continent many were in separately built towers. In Langford Church, Oxfordshire, is a large VERGE clock still working, with its original stone WEIGHTS. *See* **Salisbury Cathedral Clock.**

Circular Error To remain accurate regardless of the angle it swings through (ISOCHRONOUS), a pendulum should swing in a CYCLOIDAL CURVE. It actually swings in an arc, and takes longer to swing in a large arc than a small one. The circular error is the loss in time caused by swinging in a circular path. At an arc of 10° it is about −40 sec. a day. Christiaan HUYGENS discovered this and invented CYCLOIDAL CHEEKS to eliminate it. Accurate clock pendulums are designed to swing through a total arc about $1\frac{1}{2}$° so that the error is negligible. The recoil of an ANCHOR ESCAPEMENT tends to compensate for the circular error for ordinary purposes. *See* **Escapement Error.**

Cleaning Misleading term used by watch and clockmakers for servicing, which actually involves stripping, examination, cleaning of individual parts by CLEANING MACHINE, perhaps with ULTRASONIC unit, reassembling, oiling, readjustment, and regulation by RATE RECORDER. OIL dries out after about two years and forms a soap which may act as a grinding paste with dust. After removal of this and re-oiling and greasing, the watch usually has a different RATE.

Cleaning Machine Old craftsmen used to, and still do, clean clocks and watches by hand, starting with cleaning fluids, then a paste of powdered chalk brushed on and off, and finally finishing the PIVOT holes with PEGWOOD, and the pivots with PITH. Now machines are usually employed, especially for watches, which are stripped and the main parts put in a gauze basket which is oscillated in a series of special cleaning fluids and dried in a drying chamber. Some machines are automatic. *See* **Ultrasonic Cleaning.**

Clepsydra A WATER CLOCK; literally, 'stealer of time'.

Clerkenwell Traditional home of watch and clock manufacturing in London, although many early clockmakers, such as TOMPION, GRAHAM, and MUDGE, were in Fleet Street. Now there is no major manufacturing in Clerkenwell, except for one firm of tower clock makers in Bowling Green Lane, and many watch and clock traders have joined the diamond dealers in Hatton Garden. The peak of Clerkenwell's manufacture of ENGLISH LEVERS was in the first half of the nineteenth century when 20,000 craftsmen were employed.

Click Traditional horological name for the pawl of a pawl and ratchet mechanism. *See* **Recoiling Click** *and* Fig. 26.

Clock From *clokka*, a bell. The first mechanical clock of which there is definite evidence was put up in 1335 on the church of Beata Vergine (now San Gottardo), Milan. It struck a bell at every hour up to 24, having no dial, and may have been the first public clock. The first printed illustration of a MOVEMENT was in a book by Girolamo Cardan (inventor of the cardan joint) in 1557. Earliest references to 'clok' and 'clocke' are in 1371 and 'clokkemaker' in 1390.

Clock Manor Museum Museum at Manor Heights, Bergen Park, Colorado, U.S.A., of wide range of clocks from many countries. Founded by Orville R. Hagans, 1961.

Clock Star The rotation of the Earth, and therefore time, can be more accurately measured from one or more of the 'fixed stars' than from the Sun, so such stars are called 'clock stars'. *See* **Transit Instrument, Sidereal Time** *and* **Time Determination.**

Clock-Watch Early watch that strikes like a clock. Some had repeater mechanisms, but with an extra TRAIN of wheels that

43

had to be wound separately. A REPEATER WATCH also strikes, but only when required to.

Clock Winder   Man who winds and looks after clocks, either domestic ones in large houses or TOWER CLOCKS, which often take many hours to wind after climbing hundreds of steps. Most tower clocks now have AUTOMATIC CLOCK WINDING or are being converted to it.

Clockmaker   Once a maker of clocks and watches who was recognized by his craft guild. Now a clock repairer. Clockmaking requires skills and knowledge different from watchmaking.

Clockmakers Company   The Worshipful Company of Clockmakers is No. 61 in the City of London craft guilds, its Charter having been granted on 22 August 1631. First Master was David RAMSAY. All famous past craftsmen were Freemen or Liverymen. Its Charter enabled the Company to enter any premises in and around London City to seize and destroy any faulty work, or work not done by someone who had not served his APPRENTICESHIP. Foreigners could only work with Company members, and foreign timepieces and sundials had to be approved before sale. It no longer controls the trade, but is advisory and social, has a fine library, and the GUILDHALL MUSEUM COLLECTION. It publishes lists of past apprentices and awards the TOMPION MEDAL. Those appointed to the Livery still include well-known horologists. Address: Candlewick House, 116 Cannon Street, London, E.C.1.

Club Tooth   Special shape of ESCAPE WHEEL TOOTH employed with the LEVER ESCAPEMENT to increase the length of IMPULSE while decreasing wear (Fig. 17).

Coaching Clock   Wall timekeeper with large dial, round or hexagonal, 2 to 3 ft. in diameter, used by coaching inns in the eighteenth century, for the benefit of travellers. Also called a TAVERN CLOCK, and later an ACT OF PARLIAMENT CLOCK. The dials were usually black or green with gold numerals and had no glass. Usually there was a SECONDS PENDULUM. Many are still in existence in inns south of London. One inn opposite Canterbury Cathedral has two (Fig. 29).

Cock   A metal bar which carries one or more PIVOT bearings and is fixed at one end only. Looks like half a BRIDGE.

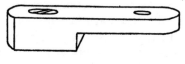

Fig. 9. Cock.

Cocktail Watch   Fancy watch for women. Usually the UNBREAKABLE GLASS is thick and lens-like and called a 'cocktail glass'.

Coin Watch   A gold coin, usually a Napoleon or a Marie Louise, with an extremely thin watch movement and dial concealed inside it. The coin is hollowed out and hinged, and opened by a hidden catch. Wonderful technical achievements by several Swiss manufacturers.

Cole, James Ferguson (1799–1880)   One of the finest of English clock and watch makers, and one of the last who could make every part of the MOVEMENT and CASE himself, even to engraving. Sometimes called the 'English BREGUET' because he exchanged ideas with Breguet. At the Five Centuries of British Timekeeping Exhibition in London, 1955, there was a special pocket CHRONOMETER he made when he was under 21, and a special LEVER WATCH made when he was 72.

Collections In *England* the main collections of clocks and watches that are on exhibition are those of the ASHMOLEAN MUSEUM, Oxford; BRITISH MUSEUM; Fitzwilliam Museum, Cambridge; Gershom Parkington, Bury St Edmunds; GUILD-HALL MUSEUM; Museum of the History of Science, Oxford; NATIONAL MARITIME MUSEUM; Royal United Service Museum; SCIENCE MUSEUM; Basingstoke Museum; and WALLACE COL-LECTION. Abroad there are collections: In *Austria*—Kunsthistorisches Museum, Technisches Museum, Schatz des Deutschen Rittordens, Oesterreishes Museum fur Angewandte Kunst, Uhren Museum der Stadt (Vienna Clock Museum), all in Vienna, and the Steirisches Landesmuseum, Graz; In *Denmark*—Rosenborg Castle, National Museet, both in Copenhagen. In *France*—the Louvre, Conservatoire Nationale des Arts et Metiers, Musée des Arts Decoratifs, all in Paris, and the Musée de Besançon. In *West Germany*—Bayerisches National Museum, Munich; Germanisches Museum, Nuremberg; Wurttembergisches Landesmuseum, Stuttgart; Hessisches Landesmuseum, Kassel; Mainfrankisches Museum, Würzberg; Kienzle Museum. In *East Germany*—the Staat. Math. Phys. Salon, and Zwinger, Dresden. In *Holland*—Rijksmuseum, Gemeentemuseum, both in Amsterdam; Rijksmuseum voor de Geschiedenis der Natuurwetonschappen, Leiden. In *Switzerland*—Musée d'Art et Histoire, Geneva; Historisches Museum, Basle; Musée d'Horlogerie, La Chaux de Fonds. In the *U.S.A.*—Metropolitan Museum of Art, New York; Columbia Museum of Horological Antiquities, Pa.; CLOCK MANOR MUSEUM, Colorado; American Museum of Clocks and Watches, New York 53; Franklin Institute, Pa.; U.S. National Museum (Smithsonian), Washington 25; California Academy of Sciences, San Francisco 18; Berenice Bishop Museum, Honolulu.

Columbus Clock Souvenir clock made almost entirely of wood, but imitating a fifteenth-century VERGE and FOLIOT iron clock. Probably first made in the Black Forest, Germany, for the Chicago Exhibition of 1892 to commemorate the 400th anniversary of the landing of Columbus and later mass produced in the U.S.A. A picture of Columbus and the date 1492 which are embossed on the wooden dial have misled gullible 'antique' buyers. There are variations, some with Mozart's picture, and others with a fir tree and the date 1640.

Column Clock   Clock with a base like an architectural column. *See* **Pillar Clock.**

Compass Sundial   Type of PORTABLE SUNDIAL, similar to a fixed SUNDIAL, which was set up by a compass and then showed SOLAR TIME by the position east or west of the sun in the sky.

Compensation Balance   A BALANCE designed to correct TEMPERATURE ERROR, when used with a particular type of HAIRSPRING. The earliest attempts at TEMPERATURE COMPENSATION were by controlling the force of the hairspring. First to compensate the balance was LE ROY, who fixed to it two mercury thermometers, expanding inwards. At higher temperatures a balance goes slower; the thermometers made it tend to go faster as temperature rose. He improved on this by using a balance wheel rim of two semicircular BI-METALLIC strips, each carrying a weight one end and being fixed to the balance arm at the other. This is called a 'cut balance' (Fig. 5) and was much improved in the EARNSHAW BALANCE. In heat, the ends of the bi-metallic strips moved the weights towards the centre of the balance. The compensation, however, introduced a MIDDLE TEMPERATURE ERROR which attempts were made to eliminate by AUXILIARY COMPENSATION. This error is only serious on timepieces like MARINE CHRONOMETERS submitted to extremes of temperature. Most successful was the GUILLAUME BALANCE, which has the rim made of a special bi-metallic strip

47

to give almost perfect compensation with a steel hairspring. Other forms are the DITISHEIM BALANCE and the OVALIZING BALANCE, also for use with special hairsprings. The cut balance used in high-grade watches has screws round the rim which act as weights and can be screwed in or out to adjust temperature compensation, timekeeping, and POISE. Introduction of the alloy ELINVAR simplified the entire problem by enabling the hairspring to be effectively compensated, so that a plain uncut brass balance could again be employed. Since 1930, various other hairspring alloys such as Metalinvar, NIVAROX, Isoval, Durinval, and Nispan-C have been invented to give excellent compensation with plain uncut balances of nickel, or a beryllium alloy such as GLUCYDUR. Many millions of cheap watches, however, are still made with useless dummy compensation balances, which is fraudulent.

Compensation Curb The second attempt at TEMPERATURE COMPENSATION of a BALANCE and SPRING by HARRISON in mid-eighteenth century. A BI-METALLIC strip effectively shortens the length of the hairspring by moving two CURB PINS along it as temperature rises.

Compensation Pendulum A PENDULUM that has been compensated for TEMPERATURE ERROR. In 1721, GRAHAM made a pendulum with a jar of mercury of particular size for its BOB. The mercury expands upwards to compensate for the rod expanding downwards. This was followed by HARRISON's cheaper version of steel and brass rods, the GRIDIRON PENDULUM. Another combination of metals is zinc and steel (*see* **Riefler Clock**). Pendulum rods are also made of wood, such as Fir, dried out and varnished, as its expansion coefficient is small. Perfect compensation, however, was not achieved until GUILLAUME discovered INVAR, a metal alloy that remains the same length at different temperatures. *See* **Temperature Error.**

Complicated Watch Watch with COMPLICATED WORK. The most complicated watch in the world is said to be one, still existing, made by LE ROY in 1896. It has a PERPETUAL CALENDAR giving date, day, month, and year for 100 years, phases and age of the moon, seasons, solstices, equinoxes, and EQUATION OF TIME; there is a CHRONOGRAPH with FLY BACK, minute and hour counters, and UP-AND-DOWN DIAL: it will strike GRANDE SONNERIE, or ordinarily, or be silent; there is a MINUTE REPEATER on three notes; SIDEREAL gearing operates ASTRONOMICAL DIALS for Paris and Lisbon (where the first owner lived) and LOCAL TIMES are given for 125 of the world's towns; sunrise and sunset times for Lisbon are shown, and a thermometer, hygrometer, barometer, and compass are incorporated. The watch can be regulated without being opened (Plate 4). Only about three manufacturers still make really complicated watches, which can cost over £3,000 each.

Complicated Work Any mechanism other than simple time-of-day in a clock or watch, such as ASTRONOMICAL, CHRONO-GRAPH, and REPEATER. Watches with SELF-WINDING work, simple CALENDAR or ALARM, are so common today, however, that they are not regarded as complicated.

Compound Pendulum A pendulum which has a weight on each end of its rod and is suspended near the centre. It swings very slowly. Used in the metronome and very rarely in clocks.

Comptoise Clock Alternative name for a MORBIER CLOCK, after the district where the village Morbier is situated.

Condensation A watch case that is not completely air-tight or WATERPROOF, will 'breathe' as its temperature changes. If it draws in perspiration from the wrist, or other moisture, a drop in temperature will make this condense inside the glass and on the steel parts, causing rust. The air in a waterproof watch contains so little moisture that sudden chilling can only produce a milky haze on the glass. The answer to this is to seal the watch in very dry air, although one Swiss maker produces vacuum-sealed watches.

Congreve Clock   A ROLLING BALL CLOCK in which the ball is the timekeeper, invented by Wm. Congreve in 1808. The ball runs down a zigzag track on a metal table (indicating seconds by passing under bridges). The table is tilted the opposite way every half-minute to send the ball back to the other end. Tilting is effected by clockwork, released by the ball striking catches at each end of the track. Hours and minutes are shown on dials. It has been calculated that the steel ball rolls about 12,500 miles a year (Plate 6).

Conical Pendulum   Pendulum that swings in a circle, invented by Jost Bodeker in 1587. Used as a speed governor, or CHRONOSCOPE, by Siemens and AIRY for training a telescope on a moving star. Also used for novelty clocks, one of which has the MOVEMENT in, and dial on, the ball-shaped pendulum BOB. A disadvantage is the large CIRCULAR ERROR.

Conical Pivot   Elementary cone-shaped PIVOT used in alarm clocks, cheap watches, and meters. Runs in a CUP BEARING and usually employed for the BALANCE only in timekeepers. Wear of these pivots often explains why an alarm will only run dial downwards.

Constant Force Escapement   An ESCAPEMENT designed to give exact measured IMPULSES to a BALANCE and SPRING or a PENDULUM, and thus avoid changes in RATE caused by variations in the driving force. *See* **Remontoire** *and* **Gravity Escapement.**

Contrate Wheel   Cup-shaped wheel with its teeth cut in the rim of the cup so that they are at right angles to the wheel.

Used with normal PINION (gear) to drive through a right angle. Simple alternative to a bevel gear. Used with the modern PLATFORM ESCAPEMENT and on some VERGE clocks and watches (Plate 2).

Conversion As each improvement to timekeeping was invented, such as the PENDULUM, ANCHOR ESCAPEMENT, HAIR-SPRING, LEVER ESCAPEMENT, etc., many older timepieces were converted. This often makes it difficult to date antique pieces. As accurate modern timepieces are so plentiful, it is considered vandalism to convert an antique. Yet people still commit the heresy of removing an antique MOVEMENT in favour of a synchronous electric one.

Cordless Clock   American name for a BATTERY CLOCK.

Cotehele Clock   Ancient TOWER CLOCK with iron wheels set in a row in a vertical iron frame fixed to a wooden post, with the VERGE and FOLIOT at the bottom. It is in the chapel of Cotehele House, near Calstock, Cornwall, which belongs to the National Trust. *See* **Vertical Frame.**

Count Down   Method of announcing time still available before an event, particularly the firing of a rocket, by counting backwards first in hours, minutes, then seconds until the last '3, 2, 1, fire', using a large special TIMER.

Count Wheel   Correct name for what is usually called the LOCKING PLATE since it counts the strokes of striking.

Coventry   One of the centres of the earlier BRITISH HORO-LOGICAL INDUSTRY, with CLERKENWELL and PRESCOT. Watch-making started here in the early eighteenth century and up to 1860 a big trade was carried on with the U.S.A. RAW MOVEMENTS came from Prescot, and went through the hands of the 'first half doer', the 'escapement doer', the 'finisher', the 'timer', and the 'examiner'. The Coventry trade was killed in the late nineteenth century by the craftsmen refusing to accept machine finishing methods and only one firm still thrives there, although it gave up making watches when the factory was blown up in World War Two. Coventry watchmakers were once easily recognized in the street by their top hats, white aprons rolled up to the waist, and eyeglasses hanging round their necks.

Cox, James (1760–88) English clock and watchmaker who specialized in COMPLICATED WORK and in exporting to oriental countries. He ran a museum of SINGING BIRDS, unusual clocks with AUTOMATA, and mechanical toys, in London.

Craftsmanship Test A performance test for watches carried out by the NATIONAL PHYSICAL LABORATORY. It replaced the KEW 'A' CERTIFICATE tests. *See* **Rating Certificate.**

Cratzer, Nicholas Henry VIII's ROYAL CLOCKMAKER, who made the ANNE BOLEYN CLOCK. A letter of 12 October 1520, to Cardinal Wolsey, suggested using Cratzer as a spy in Germany.

Cromwellian Clock Another name for a LANTERN CLOCK.

Cross-Beat Escapement A more accurate VERGE ESCAPEMENT having two springy balance arms swinging across each other on nearly the same centre. Invented by Jobst BURGI about 1586, but only 'rediscovered' in 1953 (by Dr H. von Bertele). Also called a 'double balance'.

Crown Wheel The ESCAPE WHEEL of a VERGE ESCAPEMENT (Fig. 12), which is therefore also called 'crown wheel escapement'. It is a form of CONTRATE WHEEL with pointed teeth, which give it the appearance of a king's crown. It lasted in clock and watch escapements for 400 years until the ANCHOR ESCAPEMENT made it unnecessary in clocks and the CYLINDER and other escapements ousted it from watches (Plate 2).

Crucifix Clock   Clock combined with a model of the Christian crucifixion; made in seventeenth century.

Cruciform Watch   Watch with a case the shape of a cross, i.e. a FORM WATCH (Plate 4).

Crutch   Connecting member between the ESCAPEMENT of a clock and its PENDULUM, allowing domination by the pendulum. Invented by Christiaan HUYGENS in 1657 (Fig. 27).

Crystal   An unbreakable watch GLASS.

Ctesibius   Mathematician of 200 B.C. who was first to design a water clock to show hours of varying duration (TEMPORAL HOURS) during the year.

Cuckoo Clock   Clock in which a wooden cuckoo calls the hours by popping out of a door at the hour, its call being imitated by pipes and air bellows. The earliest extant of about 1775 is of wood with a VERGE ESCAPEMENT and pendulum in front of the dial. It strikes half hours on a glass bell. The inventor may have been Anton Ketterer, of Schonwald in the Black Forest, some 40 years earlier. Later ones have carved wooden cases, metal MOVEMENTS, short pendulums, two metal 'fir cone' weights, and run for 30 hours. Cuckoo clocks are often but quite wrongly supposed to be Swiss in origin and make.

Cuckoo-Quail Clock   A CUCKOO CLOCK which also imitates the sound of the quail. Another version has a trumpeter as well as a cuckoo.

53

Cup Bearings Cone-shaped depressions in the end of a steel screw or plug, associated with the CONICAL PIVOTS of the BALANCES of 30-hr. alarm clocks and cheap watches. For electric supply and other meters, the cup bearings are often of synthetic ruby.

Curb Pins To make small changes in the RATE of a watch, the outer end of the HAIRSPRING runs between two closely spaced 'curb pins' on the INDEX (Fig. 15), so that moving the index in effect alters the length of the hairspring.

Cut Balance A temperature COMPENSATION BALANCE with a BI-METALLIC rim. The rim is cut to form two semicircles, each being fastened at one end to the arm of the balance wheel. Larger cut balances which carry weights on the ends of the arms tend to be affected by the weights trying to swing outwards under centrifugal force, so that they are not truly ISOCHRONOUS. *See* Fig. 5 *and* **Bi-Metallic Balance.**

Cycloidal Cheeks Curved plates each side of the suspension of a PENDULUM to make it swing in a cycloid instead of an arc, thus avoiding CIRCULAR ERROR. Invented by HUYGENS.

Cylinder Escapement Form of ESCAPEMENT perfected by George GRAHAM in 1725 with a half cylinder on the BALANCE STAFF which releases and is IMPULSED by the ESCAPE WHEEL teeth. It replaced the VERGE ESCAPEMENT, and came into its own again in the nineteenth century for machine-made cheap watches and clocks, until replaced by the PIN LEVER. Also called the 'HORIZONTAL ESCAPEMENT'.

Cylindrical Spring POCKET CHRONOMETERS (except Swiss ones) and MARINE CHRONOMETERS have BALANCE SPRINGS that are HELICAL in shape with incurved ends (instead of being flat spirals) because early makers found these had better RATES.

First patented by ARNOLD in 1775. The present Mercer marine chronometer has a helical balance spring made of an alloy of the precious metal palladium. Springs of quartz glass have also been made. The FLOATING BALANCE is suspended from a helical balance spring half of which is wound clockwise and half anti-clockwise to prevent the balance from rising and falling. A few pocket watches have also been made with cylindrical MAINSPRINGS.

Danish Clocks   A forgotten treasury of magnificent clocks was recognized in Rosenborg and Frederiksborg castles and the Princes Palace in 1953 by H. von Bertele and H. Steisdal. These revealed an early and advanced culture.

Daylight Saving   Introduction of the Summer Time Act of 1925 putting on clocks in summer to give an extra hour of daylight was almost entirely due to William Willett (d. 1915), a London builder. While Britain dallied, Willett's pamphlet on his ideas was translated into French and German and the Germans introduced the system during the First World War from 1914–18 for economy of lighting. The British followed from 1916–18. A sundial memorial to Willett in Petts Wood, Kent, always shows summer time.

De Vick's Clock   One of the earliest known clocks, made by Henry de Vick, of Paris, for King Charles V of France in 1371. It has been heavily restored and is in the wall on a corner of the Palais de Justice.

Dead Beat   Moving in definite jumps without recoiling, as with the seconds hand of a clock with DEAD BEAT ESCAPEMENT, a SLAVE DIAL, or an INDEPENDENT SECONDS watch.

Dead Beat Escapement   More accurate form of ANCHOR ESCAPEMENT that does not RECOIL. Invented by George GRAHAM

55

in 1715 and still used for REGULATORS and other precision clocks. The PALLETS are often jewelled.

Decimal Time   The French Revolutionaries in 1793 established decimal (or Republican) time as well as decimal weights and measures. A decimal hour was to have 100 minutes. Some clocks and watches with decimal dials were made, but even the zeal of the revolutionaries did not ensure their popularity. A Revolutionary calendar with months of 30 days each and no weeks was also introduced. Each month was named after the weather, e.g. Brumaire (fog) was November, and divided into three periods of ten days called 'decades'.

Decimal Timer   A TIMER calibrated with 100 instead of 60 divisions to the minute. Used for certain industrial purposes where it is more convenient to count in decimals.

Deck Watch   Because a ship's MARINE CHRONOMETER is moved as little as possible to avoid disturbing its RATE, a precision watch is compared with it and used on the deck for observations during NAVIGATION. Such a deck watch is like a large pocket watch, but is kept in a special box, like that for the chronometer, to avoid disturbing it unnecessarily. Originally fitted with a DETENT ESCAPEMENT, but now has a LEVER ESCAPEMENT.

Defroster Time Switch   A TIME SWITCH driven by a SYNCHRONOUS CLOCK motor that switches off a deep freeze refrigerator for $\frac{1}{4}$ hr. or longer every six hours to keep it defrosted without damaging the contents.

Degree Plate   Small plate marked in degrees, and seconds of a degree, and fixed to the back of a clock case behind a pointer on the end of a pendulum, to show the amplitude or angle of swing. Used on REGULATORS, TOWER CLOCKS, MASTER CLOCKS, and other PRECISION CLOCKS. VULLIAMY claimed to have invented it. Also called a 'beat plate'.

Demagnetizer A coil of wire carrying an alternating current from the electric mains and used for demagnetizing watches that have been affected by MAGNETISM. The watch is held in or over the coil and the alternating electro-magnetic field causes rapid reversal of the magnetism in the watch which is reduced to zero as the watch is withdrawn from the influence of the coil.

Dennison, Aaron L. The pioneer of machine-made watches in Roxburg, U.S.A., in 1850. Later set up at Waltham in 1856, then moved to England where he set up the English Watch Co. The firm of Dennison is now a prominent English maker of watch cases. The original Dennison Watch Collection belonging to the Waltham Watch Co. was sold at Christies, London, for £13,680 in 1961.

Detached Escapement An ESCAPEMENT in which the oscillating element (PENDULUM or BALANCE AND SPRING) is almost entirely free of the mechanism which it controls, as in the LEVER and DETENT ESCAPEMENTS, and the FREE PENDULUM. Escapements with FRICTIONAL REST are not detached.

Detent A *detente* is the 'end of strained relations'. A detent is a lever that holds up a spring or locks something; a pawl is one, for example. Used particularly for the lever associated with the DETENT ESCAPEMENT.

Detent Escapement An accurate DETACHED ESCAPEMENT in which the BALANCE WHEEL is impulsed in one direction only. During its swing, the balance wheel moves aside a DETENT which releases one tooth of the ESCAPE WHEEL. This tooth gives the balance wheel a push in the direction in which it is going and is then locked. On the return swing of the balance a so-called 'passing-spring' prevents the escape wheel from being unlocked. As the BEAT of MARINE CHRONOMETERS is usually half a second and the escape wheel moves at every other beat, the seconds hand shows DEAD BEAT seconds. Invented for use on ships at sea by Thos. MUDGE, Thos. EARNSHAW, and LE ROY in the early eighteenth century. Also called the 'chronometer escapement'. *See* **Spring Detent.**

Dial, Clock   Before about 1400, a clock dial revolved to show the time against a fixed hand. Soon a moving hand became almost universal with a fixed dial of iron, silver, brass, wood, and other materials. Only hours, half hours, and perhaps quarters were shown. Early BRACKET and LONG CASE CLOCKS had rectangular dials of brass with CHAPTER RINGS and corner SPANDRELS first engraved then as separate parts fixed by screws. As soon as the MINUTE HAND came into use, minute divisions appeared, often prominently marked. The numerals and time divisions were engraved and filled with black wax, and chapter rings often SILVERED, and the dial centres MATTED. In front of the dial was a door with a rectangular glass. The square dial gave way to the BREAK ARCH, and after 1750 a door with a round glass began to be used, which made the square dial behind it appear round and did away with the necessity for spandrels. At the end of that century, the round 'door', comprising just a BEZEL with a glass in it, appeared and has continued to today. Dials also became silvered all over and the separate chapter ring disappeared. Painted dials on sheet metal and also enamelled dials came in at about the same time, although enamelled ones were rare on clocks because of the size. Painted dials with scenes and animals or birds became common on long case clocks after 1800. Dials today are of almost any material, the most common being silvered brass, anodized aluminium, wood, GRAINED brass, ceramic, card or paper on various sheet metals, glass, or plastics with the CHAPTERS painted or printed on, or embossed, or separately made and fastened in place. Dials of TOWER CLOCKS may be of cast iron, copper, aluminium, bronze, concrete, stone, glass, etc.

Dial Painter   Only large dials and special ones are painted today. At one time, many, including enamelled ones, had hand-painted hour and minute symbols. Incredible skill was shown on watch dials of a century and more ago, a magnifying glass being necessary to read the fine lettering of the signatures. Painters of TOWER CLOCK dials sometimes employ gold leaf for the numerals; such a painter reckons never to restore the same dial twice as gold leaf lasts more than a generation. Certain painters in the past specialized in decorating dials. *See* **Enamelled Watch, Limoges Enamel** *and* **Huaud.**

Dial, Watch   Early watch dials were of gilded metal engraved with numerals. Sometimes the numerals were engraved on a separate silver CHAPTER RING. Occasionally the whole dial was silver. ENAMELLED WATCH dials were introduced in the sixteenth century, some painted, others champlevé (inlaid enamel). Today dials are silvered or gilded brass, with matt, brushed, polished, or other finish. The numerals or BATONS are printed on, embossed, or metal pieces separately made and applied. There are as many as 40 processes in making a dial. Finest dials are of gold, and for novelty other materials such as leather, veneered wood, and linen have been employed.

Dialling   Mathematical construction of sundials. In the seventeenth century dialling was the basis of many recreational problems such as working out the bounds of land by tree shadows.

Diamond Watch   Any watch of which the case and/or the bracelet is set with diamonds for decoration. Diamonds were once used for JEWEL bearings, particularly END STONES.

Digital Indication   Time indication by figures instead of hands, thus 9.32, as in a TICKET CLOCK or ELECTRONIC CHRONOMETER. Strictly, digital means in separate steps, so any watch hand is digital, but a SYNCHRONOUS CLOCK hand is not (Fig. 30).

Directoire Clock   French style of clock from 1795–99 of various neo-classic designs (also clocks of the period after the Revolution when various experiments were made to show DECIMAL TIME).

Ditisheim, Paul (b. 1865)   Fine watchmaker who collaborated with GUILLAUME in developing alloys for precision timekeeping and produced an accurate BALANCE of his own. Also developed modern watch OILS. *See* **Epilame.**

Ditisheim Balance   A SOLID BALANCE with small separate BI-METALLIC blades for TEMPERATURE COMPENSATION. Invented by DITISHEIM, of Switzerland, in 1920, for use with a HAIRSPRING of ELINVAR. This overcame centrifugal troubles of the CUT BALANCE and the magnetic weakness of a steel hairspring.

Diver's Watch   Time intervals are very important to skin divers using limited air supplies and having to be careful of 'decompression times'. Specially WATERPROOFED watches are made for them. These also have large LUMINOUS numerals and hands and an ELAPSED TIME INDICATION by rotating the BEZEL, which is marked in minutes and quarter hours.

Dollar Watch   Robert Ingersoll sold a number of things for a dollar each, including a printing outfit and a camera, and in 1894 produced his first watch at this low price, 'the watch that made the dollar famous'! In England it was called the 'crown' and sold for five shillings.

Domestic Clock Any type of clock for the home. The earliest was the HOUSE CLOCK.

Dondi's Clock First astronomical clock of which complete constructional details are known. Built originally in 1348–64 in Pavia, Italy, it had a 24-hr. dial with fixed hand and elaborate indications, including the first continuous recording of minutes, first dials showing sunrise and sunset, day of the month, annual calendar, conversion of MEAN TIME to SIDEREAL TIME, trajectories of planets, etc. An exact model was made in 1960 by Thwaites and Reed of London, under the instruction of H. Alan Lloyd, for the Smithsonian Institution, U.S.A.

Dormant Jewel Fraudulent name invented by advertising men to make useless watch JEWELS seem important to gullible buyers.

Double Balance An early name for the CROSS-BEAT ESCAPE-MENT.

Double Summer Time Introduced in Britain during the Second World War for economy. In winter the clock was one hour in advance of GREENWICH MEAN TIME and in summer, two hours in advance of it.

Dover Castle Clock Large iron clock with original VERGE and FOLIOT from Dover Castle, now in the SCIENCE MUSEUM, London. Once thought to have been made in 1348, but possibly made late in the sixteenth or early in the seventeenth century, in fourteenth-century style.

Draw A LEVER ESCAPEMENT is in the locked position most of the time. To keep it so and prevent it from 'tripping', the angle of the PALLETS is set to 'draw' them into the teeth of the ESCAPE WHEEL when the two are engaged. Invented by Josiah Emery. *See* **Queen Charlotte's Watch** *and* Fig. 17.

Drum Clock Clock movement in a brass drum-shaped container—like a can of beans—with a glass in the front and lid at the back. The drum fitted into the clock case. Used in many French clocks (Plate 3).

Drum Watch After the last quarter of the sixteenth century, watches became drum-shaped, like TABLE CLOCKS. The earliest had separate lids, like boxes, but later lids were hinged. Soon the backs and front covers became more domed and the sides of many curved. The drum watch had one heavy hand, no glass, and knobs at the hours for feeling the time in the dark. Also called 'TAMBOUR' or 'cannister'.

Dumb Repeater A REPEATER WATCH for deaf people. The concussion of the blows could be felt on the case. Made in the eighteenth century.

Duplex A FRICTIONAL REST ESCAPEMENT probably invented by LE ROY about 1750. Widely used in the best English watches during the first half of the nineteenth century when good time-keeping results were obtained with it. Supplanted eventually by the CHRONOMETER and LEVER ESCAPEMENTS, but continued to be used in some machine-made American pocket watches. The ESCAPE WHEEL has two sets of teeth, one for LOCKING and one for IMPULSE (some Continental versions have two escape wheels). Impulse is given to an impulse PALLET on the BALANCE STAFF. *See* **Chinese Duplex.**

Dust Cap Special cover, usually of brass, which clipped over some eighteenth-century watch MOVEMENTS inside the case.

Dutch Clock Distinctive style of weight-driven clock standing on a wall bracket. Made in Zaandam and Friesland at the beginning of the eighteenth century. Has elaborate carving around the clock and top of the wall bracket, two hands and no glass. Also the name for a form of clock made in the Black Forest, Germany, 'deutsch' having been mistranslated. The 'staartklok' is another typical early Dutch clock. It hangs on the wall and looks like a HOODED CLOCK, but has a SECONDS PENDULUM in its case with the weights hanging in front of the case.

Dutch Striking   As well as striking ordinarily at the hour, the clock strikes the next hour on a higher-toned bell every half hour. Found in Dutch and German clocks. Some early TABLE CLOCKS sounded the previous hour at the half hour.

Dutch Wag   Clock without a case hung on the wall. The short pendulum wags quickly beneath it. Also called 'wag on the wall'.

Earnshaw, Thomas (1749–1829)   Famous maker born in Ashton-under-Lyne, partly self-taught. Developed the MARINE CHRONOMETER and claimed ARNOLD stole his DETENT ESCAPEMENT. Made pocket chronometers and some clocks.

Earnshaw Balance   A BI-METALLIC BALANCE of brass fused on to steel, invented by Thos. EARNSHAW.

Earth Path Indicator   An astronaut in a space capsule orbiting the Earth at 17,000 to 18,000 m.p.h. has to know where he is to make a safe descent. The Earth Path Indicator made for the U.S. Mercury Man in Space project is a clock which shows a model of the Earth as it appears to revolve below him.

East, Edward (1602–97)   Maker of fine clocks and watches. Probably born at Southill near TOMPION's birthplace. Followed David RAMSAY as Royal watchmaker to Kings Charles I and II. Lived in Pall Mall near the King's tennis courts. May have introduced NIGHT CLOCKS to England.

Ebauche Unfinished watch MOVEMENT. In Switzerland most of these are produced by special factories. Other specialist factories make mainsprings, escapements, dials, hands, etc. A third group, the 'watch factories', are FINISHERS and design and manufacture watches based on the parts they purchase. There are still factories which make a watch from start to finish, but they are few. *See* **Lepine Calibre.**

Eight-Day Clock Clock intended to be wound once a week. The extra day is for reserve.

Elapsed Time Indicator A TIMER scaled from, say 30 minutes to 0, instead of 0 to 30. The hand is turned to 0 and moves back to 30, showing the time elapsed. *See* **Telephone Time.**

Electric Clock General term for SYNCHRONOUS, electric MASTER CLOCK, BATTERY and other clocks powered by electricity.

Electric Watch Wrist-watch operated by a small battery in the case. The first practical one was produced by the Hamilton Watch Co., U.S.A., in January 1957. There is no MAINSPRING and fewer gear WHEELS than in mechanical watch. It is an excellent timekeeper. The battery is the size of an acid drop and lasts up to 18 months. Atomic batteries lasting up to five years are being developed. There are French, German, and Swiss versions. The Hamilton has a tiny coil of wire fixed to the BALANCE and a miniature switch operated by it sends a current of electricity through the coil for a few thousandths of a second. This causes a magnetic field around the coil which reacts with two small fixed magnets to give the balance a push every time it swings in one direction. Since the balance has a normal HAIRSPRING attached, it is kept swinging to and fro. The balance drives the hands by a simple ratchet system. The 'winding button' is for setting the hands and switching off the battery during storage. Although so small, the coil has 230 ft. of wire in it. Swiss and French versions have the coils fixed and they attract the arm of the swinging balance. Some Swiss watches have accumulators which can be recharged by clipping a watch to a torch battery. Consumption is under 14 micro-amps.

Electronic Chronometer   A QUARTZ CLOCK for measuring short time intervals, usually with DIGITAL INDICATION. *See* **Chronometer.**

Electronic Clock   The rather exaggerated name for a BATTERY CLOCK with pendulum and TRANSISTOR instead of mechanical switch. Correct for a QUARTZ CLOCK and an ELECTRONIC CHRONOMETER.

Electronic Watch   Newest development in accurate time-keeping, announced by the Bulova Watch Co., U.S.A., in 1960. Invented by a Swiss, Max Hetzel. Timekeeping is guaranteed to a minute a month. A tuning fork, about one inch long, is kept vibrating at 360 cycles a second by coils of 16,000 turns of wire and a miniature battery all within a normal-sized watch. A tiny pawl on the tuning fork drives a wheel of less than 1/10 in. diameter with 300 teeth, which turns the hands, without apparent jerks. There is no tick, but a high-pitched hum, and only 12 moving parts against 19 in an ordinary and 26 in a SELF-WINDING WATCH. Power consumed is 8 millionths of a watt. Also used for TIME SWITCHES in artificial satellites. There are still small, but fixed, POSITIONAL ERRORS in two positions of up to ±5 sec. a day (Plate 7).

Elinvar   Alloy for HAIRSPRINGS invented by Dr GUILLAUME and named from 'elasticité invariable' because its elasticity does not vary at different temperatures like that of spring steel. Revolutionized watch adjustment by eliminating MIDDLE TEMPERATURE ERROR and also enabled the BALANCE AND SPRING to be made NON-MAGNETIC. *See* **Compensation Balance** *and* **Temperature Compensation.**

Ellicott, John (1706–72)   Son of a fine clockmaker of the same name, he became even greater than his father, making many CYLINDER watches and clocks. Invented a form of COMPENSATION PENDULUM. Had an observatory in his private house at Hackney.

Empire Clock   French gilt clock of Greek or Egyptian style made from about 1800 to 1815. Second Empire clocks are cheap reproductions of these and were made from about 1850–70.

Enamelled Watch   Coloured enamels were used as watch decoration from earlier than 1550 in champlévé style—hollows filled with enamel. Painting in different coloured enamels was employed in Limoges from 1500–1600. The only Limoges watches now existing are in the METROPOLITAN MUSEUM, New York. Painting in colour on white enamel, which was then fired and given a transparent coat, was invented about 1630 and became supreme in Blois, France, where the best early work was done, then in Geneva, Switzerland, where it is still carried on. Finer examples are in the BRITISH MUSEUM, VICTORIA AND ALBERT MUSEUM, the LOUVRE, Paris. *See* **Huaud.**

End-to-End Striking Clock   Ancient arrangement, particularly for TOWER CLOCKS and LANTERN CLOCKS, of having the driving BARRELS for the timekeeping and striking end to end, instead of side by side, as in modern weight and spring clocks.

Endless Rope or Chain   Arrangement to provide MAINTAINING POWER for weight-driven clocks. Invented by HUYGENS about 1656. Used particularly on 30 hr. LONG CASE CLOCKS, and modern TOWER CLOCKS with AUTOMATIC CLOCK WINDING. The principle is shown in Fig. 2; the driving weight pulls on the left hand line to drive the clock. The right hand line raises the driving weight. The small weight is merely to keep the rope taut.

End Stone Flat circular bearing jewel to take the end-thrust of a PIVOT. Used particularly for watch BALANCES. Made of synthetic ruby or, in the past, diamond or natural gemstone, because of their hardness. *See* **Shock Absorber** (Fig. 24).

English Dial Fine hanging wall clock, made at the beginning of the nineteenth century, in round or octagonal wooden case, the clock looking 'all dial' with a FUSEE MOVEMENT and sometimes a small box below for the PENDULUM. Often used as office or kitchen clocks.

Fig. 10. English dial.

English Lever General name for the English watch made in the nineteenth century with a pointed toothed ESCAPE WHEEL (as opposed to the Swiss CLUB TOOTH) and LEVER ESCAPEMENT. Regarded at the time as the 'Rolls-Royce of watches'. *See* **British Horological Industry.**

Engraving All apprentices were once taught engraving, so that they could cut dials and decorate clock and watch parts, but gradually work was put out to specialist engravers. Back PLATES of clocks were once elaborately engraved, as were the dials, bottom plates, and COCKS of watches.

Ephemeris Time   Time calculated from the orbits of the Earth round the Sun (as alternative to the rotation of the Earth). In 1956 the International Committee of Weights and Measures adopted the SECOND of Ephemeris Time as the fundamental unit of time, instead of the second of Mean SOLAR TIME. It is obtained in practice from the orbital motion of the Moon round the Earth, then made available for general purposes by QUARTZ CLOCKS, ATOMIC CLOCKS, etc. *See* **Time Determination.**

Epilame   After parts of a watch have been submitted to ULTRASONIC CLEANING they are so chemically clean that oil may spread, so they are given a coating of a patent 'epilame' (stearic acid) to prevent this, a treatment devised by Dr Woog of Paris and Paul DITISHEIM before ultrasonic methods were invented.

Equal Hours   After about 1350–1400, TEMPORAL HOURS were replaced by equal hours, each hour being of the same length whether by night or day. Mechanical clocks coming into use during this time in Europe and showing equal hours were responsible. JAPANESE CLOCKS were made to show temporal hours, however, until 1873. SUNDIALS were also made to show equal hours.

Equation Dial   An extra dial on a clock showing the EQUATION OF TIME, so that a SUNDIAL could be used to set the clock to MEAN TIME. First made by TOMPION and by QUARE about 1695. It was only the accuracy of the ANCHOR ESCAPEMENT that made the difference between sundial and clock apparent.

Equation of Time   The difference between SOLAR TIME (i.e. sundial time) and mean solar time (i.e. time shown by clocks), the sundial sometimes appearing fast and sometimes slow according to the clock. Before TIME SIGNALS, accurate clocks and watches had to be set by the SUNDIAL, so the Equation of Time had to be known. This was often a printed table stuck inside the clock or watch case. Expensive clocks, such as the BATH CLOCK, had an EQUATION DIAL showing how much the sundial should be fast or slow compared with the clock. The year's equation figures are published in the ASTRONOMICAL EPHEMERIS. They vary between about $+16\frac{1}{2}$ minutes and $-14\frac{1}{4}$.

Escape Wheel   The last wheel in a GOING TRAIN, controlled by the ESCAPEMENT (Figs. 1 *and* 17).

Escapement   The rate-controlling mechanism of a timekeeper. The first recorded, made by I-Hsing, a Chinese monk, in A.D. 725, was called the 'celestial balance' and was employed to control a WATER CLOCK. The earliest mechanical escapement was the VERGE and FOLIOT probably invented in the fourteenth century. Many thousands have since been invented. Most common are the ANCHOR for PENDULUM clocks, the LEVER for clocks and watches with BALANCES, and the DETENT ESCAPEMENT for MARINE CHRONOMETERS.

Escapement Error   As soon as a PENDULUM or BALANCE is given a push to keep it swinging, its timekeeping is usually interfered with, this difference in RATE being called 'escapement error'. It was analysed by AIRY. It and CIRCULAR ERROR are sometimes opposite and tend to cancel each other.

Essen Ring   Quartz crystal cut to ring shape and used for high accuracy QUARTZ CRYSTAL CLOCKS. Developed by Louis Essen of the National Physical Laboratory. At the Post Office Research Laboratories in Dollis Hill in North London one was buried 20 metres down in London clay in a sealed canister in 1955 and is used as a standard of frequency.

Eureka Clock   Electric BATTERY CLOCK, invented in 1906, which has a very large BALANCE WHEEL driven by an electro-magnet.

Examinations   Every year the BRITISH HOROLOGICAL INSTITUTE holds four grades of examinations in centres in the U.K. and abroad, for success in which diplomas and other awards are made.

Exeter Cathedral Clock   Ancient iron TOWER CLOCK of vertical construction now restored and in the north transept of the cathedral (*see* **Vertical Frame**). Has large astronomical dial almost identical to another in Ottery St Mary Church, Devon. Both are claimed to be fourteenth century, but are much later.

Expanding Bracelet   Sometimes called a 'flexible bracelet' although these are not always expanding. Early versions were made from expanding spring links; current ones usually have a spring scissors action. A good expanding bracelet is precision made and may have over 100 parts. Some have latches for removing single links for length adjustment. Often made of gold or ROLLED GOLD or GOLD PLATED base metal with stainless steel backing.

Explorer's Watch   Watertight English pocket watch made by Dent with a DENNISON case at the end of the last century for use of explorers. The winding button and the dial were covered by screw-on caps with cork washers; this was the first successful WATERPROOFING.

Falling Ball Clock   A form of GRAVITY CLOCK invented in the seventeenth century. The clock has a ball-shaped brass case with a 24 hr. MOVING BAND which turns round its 'equator'. The hour is indicated by an image, such as a cherub, fixed to the case. A cord wound round a BARREL in the ball comes out of the top of the case. The clock is suspended from this and slowly descends—like a spider on a thread—being driven by its own weight. When it hangs low, it is raised by hand and the cord 'disappears' inside the clock, being wound back on to the barrel by a spring.

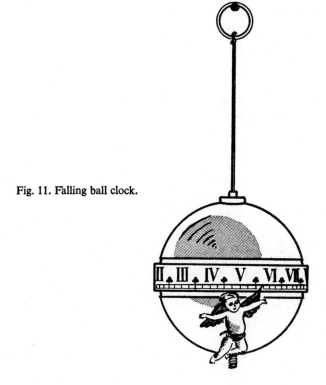

Fig. 11. Falling ball clock.

False Bob   Another name for a MOCK PENDULUM (Fig. 18).

Farmer's Watch   Large pocket watch with VERGE ESCAPEMENT and an enamelled dial showing a farming scene, made from about 1820 to as late as 1880.

Farouk Collection   Exceptional collection of watches, including some with pornographic AUTOMATA, sold after Farouk was deposed as King of Egypt.

Fellows Watch Collection   Antique watches bequeathed to the British Museum in the late nineteenth century by Sir Charles Fellows. Lady Fellows made water-coloured drawings of the watches as they were bought, before restoration, which are exceptionally beautiful and accurate and now belong to the Royal Institution, London.

Finding the Longitude   A ship has to know its position East or West by 'finding the longitude'. It is relatively easy to find the position North or South by Sun or stars; that to the East or West is complicated by rotation of the Earth and until the eighteenth century ships often sailed thousands of miles out off course and were lost. The Spanish, Dutch, Venetians, and British (in 1714) offered big prizes for methods of finding the way at sea. The British one of £20,000 was the only one paid, to John HARRISON for his marine timekeeper. The principle of using a timekeeper was this. It was set to the time at the port which the ship left, say Bristol. Suppose the ship sailed West; the Captain would compare his LOCAL TIME, obtained from observations of the Sun, with the clock's time. If there was an hour and a half's difference, he was $22\frac{1}{2}°$ west of Bristol because the Earth turns 15° in an hour. The method is still used, but the ship's MARINE CHRONOMETER is kept to GREENWICH MEAN TIME by RADIO TIME SIGNALS and compared with local time. *See* **Navigation.**

Finial   A decoration on top of a clock case, to 'finish it off'. Common types in brass were balls with points on top, flambeaux (flames), acorns and pineapples, urns, spires. They were used singly (and also called 'terminals') or in groups.

Fire Clock In Tibet and China, joss-sticks were once used for timekeeping. The stick was a strip of cane coated with a dried mixture of clay, sweet burning sawdust, and gold dust. Lit at one end, it smouldered for several days. Marks along the stick showed the hours. A fire-stick was used as an alarm by tying two little weights by a thread to the appropriate place. When the stick smouldered to that point, the thread burnt and the weights dropped with a clang into a copper bowl. *See* **Candle Clock.**

Five Minute Repeater A REPEATER CLOCK or WATCH that sounds the last hour on a lower note, the last quarter on a TING TANG, and one blow on the higher note for each 5 minutes past the quarter. Operated by a slide on the side of a watch and a pull cord on a clock.

Flamsteed, John First ASTRONOMER ROYAL, appointed in 1676, and originator of the NAUTICAL ALMANAC, now prepared in five countries. *See* **Greenwich Observatory.**

Flat Bed Type of construction of modern TURRET CLOCKS with the ARBORS (axles) in a row across a steel, or cast iron, horizontal frame. Popularized by Lord GRIMTHORPE in 'BIG BEN' in 1859, but used as early as 1763 in the church of Notre Dame, Versailles, France.

Flexible Watch Band A metal wrist-watch BRACELET that is flexible, but not an EXPANDING BRACELET. Usually of gold. There are two main forms of construction, by weaving gold wire (called 'milanese') and by closely fitting jointed links. The second type is often known as 'brick' or 'pavé'. Short rectangular tubes fitted end to end over woven wire give a similar effect. Some of these bracelets are triumphs of the jewellers' art and if given 'satinized' finish the joints are almost impossible to see. The band is normally soldered permanently to the watch case.

Floating Balance   An accurate escapement for clocks invented in Germany in 1950 but used in British clocks. The BALANCE WHEEL is suspended from its CYLINDRICAL HAIRSPRING to reduce friction, and it is FREE SPRUNG in some versions. Its advantage over the short PENDULUM clock is that it is portable and remains accurate even if the clock is tilted.

Floral Clock   Large public clock set out in bedding plants on the ground. Some strike; a few are CUCKOO CLOCKS.

Fly   A governor or rotating fan used to slow down a striking or chiming mechanism. Incorporates an elementary clutch; or ratchet freewheel on large clocks. That on a LONG CASE CLOCK is about $1\frac{1}{2}$ in. across and that on BIG BEN's clock, about 6 ft. The earliest known is on a German or Italian clock of about 1550. Some of the latest have an arrangement to decrease the area of the fan as the speed falls (i.e. as the MAINSPRING runs down) so that the intervals between strokes remain constant.

Fly Back   The arrangement which returns a hand to zero on a TIMER or CHRONOGRAPH by means of a heart-shaped cam.

Flying Pendulum Clock   Novel (and inaccurate) clock invented by P. Closon in 1883. The ESCAPEMENT is a length of thread with a ball on the end, which swings in a circle, but is interrupted each 180° by twisting and untwisting round one of two vertical rods on top of the clock. Manufacture was resumed in 1959 in Germany for a U.S.A. company.

Fob Watch   Now the name for a watch hanging on a short decorative strap, or chain, and usually combined with a brooch worn on the lapel, the watch dial being upside down so that it can be read. Originally a pocket watch on a short chain, after *fuppe*, low German for 'pocket'. A nurse's watch is often of this type. Also a CHATELAINE WATCH. For men, the 'fob chain'

74

is an alternative to the watch chain or ALBERT, and is in fact for a pocket watch.

Foliot Swinging bar with adjustable weights on the end. Employed as the earliest mechanical time controller, with a VERGE ESCAPEMENT. The bar is twisted first one way and then the other and its RATE can be increased by moving the weights on the ends towards the centre. The word was first used by Jean Froissart, the French chronicler, in 1369, and means 'to dance about madly'. *See* **Salisbury** *and* **Cassiobury Clocks.**

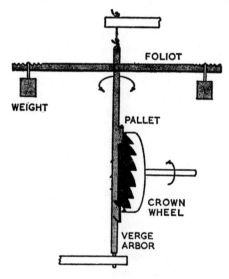

Fig. 12. Verge and foliot escapement.

Forgeries English watches were often forged on the Continent during the eighteenth century and falsely signed 'TOMPION', 'QUARE', 'GRAHAM' *et al.*, some names being misspelt. The MOVEMENTS inside were cheap and not even imitations. BREGUET's work was also forged which made him devise his

75

SECRET SIGNATURE. Clocks have been forged, but much more realistically. Not infrequently a case has become separated from its original MOVEMENT and both have been built into complete clocks, so that there are two 'genuine' antiques instead of one. Dials with famous names engraved on them have been given to inferior movements and existing movements given a new 'antique' case. There are instances, too, of an original engraved name being scraped off and new one, e.g. Thos. TOMPION, engraved in its place. The situation is further confused by the fact that in the nineteenth century many genuine makers, Barraud, Perrigal, Dwerrihouse, and others bought their 'bread-and-butter clocks' from embryo factories and had their own names engraved on dials and movements; thousands of retailers, middlemen, and even customers also had their names engraved to appear as makers. As the price goes by the name, identical clocks sell for different prices, but these are not truly fakes. On the Continent, old German STACKFREED watches have been faked in at least three places, and as recently as from after the Second World War to 1957 in Belgium. Many electrotype copies of old Augsburg clocks have been produced. There is also, apparently, an ASTROLABE 'factory' in Mexico. Among French fakes a quantity of MOVING ARM WATCHES were made in the nineteenth century in imitation of an earlier period and huge quantities of electrotype copies of earlier French clocks were made during the Second Empire from 1852 to 1870. Until about 1914 various faked WATER CLOCKS frequently bought as genuine today were listed in the catalogue of a Birmingham manufacturer. Some bear the date 1640.

Form Watch Watch made in the shape of something else, such as a crucifix, SKULL, book, globe, animal, etc. (Plate 4).

Four-Hundred Day Clock A German clock under a glass dome with a TORSION PENDULUM, which runs for a year with one winding. Invented by Anton Harder about 1880. Still made in quantity.

Frame The structure in which the wheels and other parts of a clock or watch are built. In TOWER CLOCKS it was once VERTICAL or BIRDCAGE and is now FLAT BED; in modern domestic clocks and early watches two brass PLATES are employed, and in later watches an EBAUCHE.

Free Pendulum Clock Most accurate type of pendulum clock ever made. One at the Edinburgh Observatory has kept time to within 1/10th sec. a year. Invented by R. J. Rudd (1898) and made practical by W. H. Shortt (1921). The Shortt free pendulum is kept in a vacuum chamber and has no work to do. Another (slave) pendulum, linked to it, does all the work. The linking of the two is very ingenious. The slave is set to run about 6 sec. a day slow. Every half minute it releases a GRAVITY LEVER to IMPULSE the free pendulum. Because of the geometry of this and the PALLET on which it acts the free pendulum accepts the impulse in its own time. After impulse, the gravity arm falls on a contact, which causes an electro-magnet to reset it. This contact also: (1) releases a gravity arm to impulse the slave, (2) operates the master clock dial, and (3) brings an arm into line with a piece of clock spring on the slave pendulum. When the slave pendulum is slow, the arm bends the clock spring to accelerate the slave pendulum into step with the master. The resetting of the slave's gravity arm by contacts and electro-magnet also provides the signal for operating a slave dial. Now superseded in observatories by QUARTZ CLOCKS.

French Horological Industry One of the world's oldest and may have been the first. The earliest known maker was Julien Couldray, who made two watches set in dagger handles in 1518. Early centres were Blois (*see* **Enamelled Watch**), Paris, and Lyon. When the Huguenots were persecuted, many watchmakers went to Geneva which greatly strengthened the SWISS HOROLOGICAL INDUSTRY. After the French Revolution, Laurent Megevard, backed by the government, set up an industry in Besançon. Other pioneers were JAPY and SULLY. The present industry is organized like the Swiss. There are 250 EBAUCHES manufacturers, 350 FINISHERS, and ten complete watch manufacturers centred in the Doubs, the Haute-Savoie and the Seine. The clock industry is spread throughout France and produces about 2½ million alarms and other clocks yearly. Export watches have to satisfy QUALITY STANDARDS.

Frequency Comparison Meter   Special meter used at electricity power stations to compare mains frequency with a MASTER CLOCK, so that SYNCHRONOUS CLOCKS are kept to MEAN TIME.

Friction Spring   Spring acting as a clutch for hand setting; also one for taking up backlash of a CENTRE SECONDS HAND.

Frictional Rest   Most ESCAPEMENTS release a tooth of the ESCAPE WHEEL for a fraction of a second and then hold it up. With some, like the CYLINDER ESCAPEMENT, the escape wheel tooth is held up by its resting against part of the moving BALANCE WHEEL. Such frictional rest interferes with the free swing of the balance wheel. The LEVER ESCAPEMENT locks an escape wheel tooth without touching the balance wheel, and is therefore free.

Fromanteel   Famous family of clockmakers in London, which originated from Holland. They were named Ahasuerus, John and Abraham. John learned how to make HUYGENS pendulum clocks in Holland and the Fromanteels were the first to introduce them into England in 1658. Evelyn refers to 'our famous Fromantil' in his Diary. They worked at Mosses Alley, Southwark, and at 'The Mermaid' in Lothbury.

Front Wind   Clock wound through the dial.

Frosting   The grey matt finish given to steel parts of watches by rubbing with oilstone dust in olive oil. Frosting is carried out before GILDING if a final matt surface is required.

Fusée   A MAINSPRING gives less and less power as it runs down, which affects timekeeping. The power can be equalized by a fusée—a grooved and trumpet-shaped pulley—which the mainspring BARREL drives by a chain or length of gut. (Fusée means 'thread'.) Fusée leverage increases as the mainspring runs down. Shown as early as about 1485 in Leonardo da Vinci's sketch books and still used today in the MARINE CHRONOMETER, and special clocks. *See* **Setting Up.**

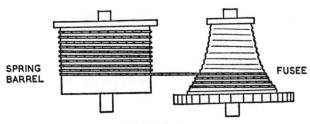

SPRING BARREL   FUSEE

Fig. 13. Fusée.

Galileo   Pioneer of experimental science who discovered that a PENDULUM kept the same time however widely it swung (*but see* **Huygens**). Invented an excellent PENDULUM-controlled ESCAPEMENT, before Huygens, but it was kept secret and constructed by his son after his death too late to influence horology.

Gas Controller   The first form of TIME SWITCH. Invented by Dr Thurgar, of Norwich, in 1867, for turning gas street lamps on and off. The first practical use of them, however, was made by a Bournemouth builder, John Gunning, for street lighting as he could not sell houses in unlit streets.

German Horological Industry   Many of the oldest clocks and watches known are German and early centres were NUREMBERG and Augsburg. An industry making WOODEN CLOCKS also grew up in the Black Forest, which popularized the CUCKOO CLOCK, but American competition nearly ruined it until Erhard Junghans re-established it on Swiss lines after 1851. Up to the Hitler war, it had one of the world's biggest outputs of clocks and watches. One main manufacturing centre for jewellery and watches, Pforzheim, was blotted out by the Royal Air Force because of the fuse making there, but has since been rebuilt, with many modern watch factories. Watch cases are also made in quantity there. The Black Forest is still the centre of a big clockmaking industry. The Germans have pioneered MAGNETIC SUSPENSION and BATTERY CLOCKS.

Gilding   Gold finish for brass used on clock and watch dials and cases. Fire gilding (also called water gilding) was done by mixing gold powder with mercury to make a paste like butter which was brushed on. The brass was washed, next heated over charcoal, and brushed, being then left matt, or alternatively polished and burnished (*see* **Frosting**). The process is dangerous to health and is rarely done now although it is the only way to restore, say, French gilt work. Electro-gilding is extensively used today for various watch parts. 'Silver gilt' is sterling silver that has had a gilding treatment.

Glass   The watch glass appeared in the eighteenth century, although some dials were protected earlier by faceted rock crystal. In our century almost all 'glasses' are unbreakable, i.e. they are plastics (such as Perspex or Plexiglas) and known to the trade as 'U/Bs', but also called 'crystals'. Transparent synthetic sapphire, often faceted on the edge, is used for some high quality small watches, as it does not become scratched. Normal glasses and U/Bs are 'sprung in' from the front, using a special tool to dome them and reduce the diameter temporarily. In WATERPROOF watches extra sealing or pressure rings are often employed with the glass.

Glass Bell Used on early CUCKOO CLOCKS. One of the last made was the case as well as the bell of a special clock with SHIP'S BELL STRIKING produced for the Festival of Britain.

Globe Clock Another name for a BALL CLOCK, but usually representing the Earth.

Gnomon The rod, pin, or wedge-shaped plate of a SUNDIAL that throws a shadow on the dial. Also called a 'style'.

Going Barrel The most common spring motor for watches and clocks. The going BARREL contains the MAINSPRING. The outer end of the mainspring is hooked inside the barrel, and the inner end is hooked to the BARREL ARBOR (i.e. the shaft through the barrel). The winding button or key turns this arbor, which winds up the spring. As the spring uncoils, it turns the barrel which has teeth round it to drive the gears. The barrel turns in the same direction as winding, and also provides its own MAINTAINING POWER (Plate 2).

Going Train The TRAIN of gears in a timekeeper controlled by the ESCAPEMENT and responsible for its timekeeping.

Gold Filled In the U.S.A. this means the best quality ROLLED GOLD. In Britain the term is disapproved of by the British Standard for watch case finishes, because it is misleading.

Gold Plated Covering of pure or alloy gold applied by an electro-chemical method. A British Standard of 1960 requires gold-plated watch cases to be marked 'P/' followed by the thickness of gold in microns (thousandths of a millimetre), thus P 15 M. *See* **Rolled Gold** *and* **Hard Gold Plating.**

Gold Watch Watch in a gold case, used because it is unaffected by acids from the skin and corrosion, as also are platinum,

ROLLED GOLD, GOLD PLATE, and STAINLESS STEEL. Silver was once commonly used for watch cases, partly for the same reason. Goldsmiths have been associated with watchmaking for 400 years.

Golden Number   New and full moons return on the same days every 19 years. The year of this cycle is calculated automatically by some early clocks. The Greeks thought so much of the calculation that they had the number written in gold. Also called the 'Metonic Cycle'.

Golf Watch   Not a watch, but a recorder that looks like one. After each stroke, the golfer pushes the 'winding button' and after each hole gives it a twist. Strokes for each hole are shown in 18 apertures around the dial. The 'minute hand' shows the number of the hole and the 'hour and seconds hands' the running total.

Gong   Metal rod, either straight or spiral, on which chimes or hours are struck. Made of steel or phosphor bronze. May have been invented by Julien LE ROY. Straight ones are used in most domestic striking and chiming clocks, but early American wall clocks and French CARRIAGE CLOCKS have spiral ones, and REPEATER WATCHES curved ones made of steel.

Gothic Clock   In the sixteenth century HOUSE CLOCKS had open iron frames of Gothic style.

Gould, R. T. (1890–1949)   Lieutenant-Commander Gould, R.N., author and broadcaster, was an authority on the MARINE CHRONOMETER (on which he wrote the standard book), typewriters, and the Loch Ness monster. He restored HARRISON's four famous timekeepers.

Graham, George (c. 1673–1751)   One of the greatest of all makers of clocks, watches, and scientific instruments. Friend of, relation by marriage, and successor to TOMPION. Invented the practical CYLINDER ESCAPEMENT for watches in 1725, the DEAD BEAT ESCAPEMENT for clocks in 1715, and MERCURIAL COMPENSATION for pendulums in 1721. Made nearly 3,000 watches, about 175 clocks, and various astronomical instruments. He was known as 'Honest George Graham'. Buried in Westminster Abbey with Tompion (Plate 2).

Grand-Daughter Clock Modern clock of grandfather style standing under about 4 ft. 6 in. high.

Grande Sonnerie Clock or watch which strikes the hour before chiming each quarter of an hour, e.g. at 3.30 it would strike three, then two quarters.

Grandfather Clock Name for a LONG CASE CLOCK which originated from a song written by the American Henry Clay Work in 1876, beginning, 'My grandfather's clock was too tall for the shelf . . .' The clock he wrote about is claimed to be that in the George Hotel, Piercebridge, North Yorkshire, but another claimant is a relative, Mrs Randolph Parker, for her clock in Granby, Massachusetts.

Grandmother Clock Like a GRANDFATHER, but under about 6 ft. high. Antique ones are extremely rare.

Grasshopper Escapement Accurate wooden ESCAPEMENT not needing oil, invented by John HARRISON, for his clocks and marine timekeepers. Modified and used later by VULLIAMY.

Gravity Arm A small lever of certain weight, pivoted at one end, for giving IMPULSES to a PENDULUM. It is normally held horizontal and released to rest on a projection on the pendulum.

After impulsing the pendulum, it is reset electrically or mechanically. *See* **Master Clock** *and* **Gravity Escapement.**

Gravity Clock   Clock driven by its own weight. Two early forms are the ROLLING (Plate 6) and the FALLING BALL CLOCK (Fig. 11). Another, made as early as 1600, is the RACK CLOCK. The Silent Keeless was one such clock; various versions have been produced in recent times.

Gravity Escapement   Accurate clock escapement in which the MAINSPRING or driving weight lifts a small lever, which drops to give IMPULSE to the PENDULUM or BALANCE, and is thus independent of the driving force. Invented by Thos. MUDGE and by Alex. Cumming around 1760–70, but not really successful until GRIMTHORPE's version of about 1852 for 'BIG BEN'. Employed in most accurate TURRET CLOCKS, ELECTRIC MASTER CLOCKS, and the FREE PENDULUM. *See* **Gravity Arm.**

Great Clock   Early name for a TOWER CLOCK. 'Great clock-maker' meant a maker of big clocks, not a famous maker.

Great Tom   The bell of a clockhouse built at Westminster after the Commonwealth, which was removed to St Paul's Cathedral by Sir Christopher Wren when the Westminster tower was pulled down in the eighteenth century. The present Great Tom is a replacement. The original one saved a soldier accused of being asleep on sentry duty at Windsor Castle from court-martial sentence. He said he heard the bell strike 13. Unlikely as this was, it proved to be true.

Great Wheel   The MAIN WHEEL of a FUSEE clock or watch.

Greenwich Civil Time   After 1925, GREENWICH MEAN TIME was reckoned from midnight instead of noon. American astronomers called this 'Greenwich Civil Time', but the British continued with G.M.T. Now both call it UNIVERSAL TIME.

Greenwich Mean Time (G.M.T.) Mean SOLAR TIME at GREENWICH OBSERVATORY. Solar times vary across the country, e.g. when it is 12 noon at Greenwich it is 11.40 a.m. at Pembroke. In 1880, G.M.T. was established by law as official time all over Great Britain. In 1884, an international conference adopted the line of longitude through Greenwich as zero MERIDIAN and the basis of TIME ZONES (on the proposition of the U.S.A., only France and Ireland voting against).

Greenwich Observatory Original building of the ROYAL GREENWICH OBSERVATORY which has been moved to Herstmonceux Castle, Sussex. The Greenwich building, including the OCTAGON ROOM, is now a museum of timekeeping and astronomical instruments. *See* **National Maritime Museum Collection.**

Gridiron Pendulum A PENDULUM compensated for TEMPERATURE ERRORS, invented by John HARRISON in 1726. A grid of alternate brass and steel rods is arranged so that in heat the expansion of one metal upwards is equal to the expansion of the other downwards, so that the pendulum remains the same length. *See* **Compensation Pendulum.**

Grimthorpe, Lord (E. B. Denison, M.A., Q.C.) The irascible lawyer and brilliant amateur clockmaker who designed 'Big Ben', the WESTMINSTER PALACE CLOCK, to which he applied his GRAVITY ESCAPEMENT, as well as other clocks. He upset clockmakers by leaving non-working parts rough, but 'Big Ben' proved not only bigger, but much more accurate than any clock previously made.

Grollier, Nicholas (1593–1686) Famous maker of ROLLING BALL CLOCKS in which the ball is the timekeeper. The invention of the practical PENDULUM clock virtually finished attempts to make the rolling ball an accurate time standard, *but see* **Congreve Clock.**

Guildhall Museum London clock and watch collection and library of the CLOCKMAKERS COMPANY with many fine specimens including MARY QUEEN OF SCOTS WATCH and the HARRISON wooden precision clock.

Guillaume, Charles-Edouard (1861–1938) Director of the International Bureau of Weights and Measures, Paris, who won the Nobel Prize in 1920 for inventing INVAR and ELINVAR, which revolutionized precision timekeeping.

Guillaume Balance A COMPENSATION BALANCE that overcomes MIDDLE TEMPERATURE ERROR by using a special nickel alloy (instead of steel) with brass for the bi-metallic rim of the CUT BALANCE. Introduced by GUILLAUME for use with a steel HAIR-SPRING in 1899, but still today at the top in TIMEKEEPING TRIALS. Also called the 'integral balance'. Weaknesses are the spring's susceptibility to magnetism and the tendency of the cut arms of the balance to fly outwards on heavy balance wheels. *See* **Compensation Balance** *and* **Ditisheim Balance.**

Guinness Clock Large public clock with AUTOMATA representing various Zoo animals in Guinness advertising. Made for the Festival of Britain Gardens, Battersea, in 1951. Eight copies were constructed followed by a number of simplified versions.

Habrecht Famous clockmaking brothers, Isaac and Josias, who completed the second STRASBOURG CLOCK in 1575. A four-foot high clock made by Isaac in 1589 in imitation of the Strasbourg clock is in the BRITISH MUSEUM COLLECTION.

Hairspring Also called 'balance spring'. A fine spring, usually spiral, applied to the BALANCE to make it much more accurate as a timekeeper. The invention was claimed by both HOOKE (in 1664) and HUYGENS (in 1675). At its inner end, the hairspring is fixed to the BALANCE STAFF by a small ring or 'collet' and a very tiny taper pin. At its outer end it is fixed to the BALANCE COCK by a stud. For simple timekeeping adjustments two CURB PINS are moved by the INDEX to alter the length of the active part of the hairspring (*see* **Regulation** *and* **Regulator**). Made of steel until ELINVAR and the other temperature compensating and non-magnetic spring were invented (*see* **Compensation Balance**). Usually made now by winding four together as a 'nest' and separating them. CYLINDRICAL SPRINGS are also employed. The outer end is sometimes raised and curved towards the centre. *See* **Breguet Spring, Free Spring** *and* **Balance and Spring.**

Half Quarter Repeater   A REPEATER WATCH or CLOCK which, when operated, strikes the last hour on a lower note, the last quarter on a TING TANG, then either nothing or a higher note to indicate that $7\frac{1}{2}$ minutes (a half quarter) has passed since the last quarter. For example, at 3.38 there would be three strokes of the lower note, two ting-tangs on the two notes, and one stroke on the higher one.

Halifax Moon   Form of MOON DIAL on which the phases of the moon are shown by a revolving globe coloured half black and half white.

Hallmark   Silver and gold watch and clock cases are assayed in Britain to determine the quality and stamped with: 1, the mark of the assaying 'hall'; 2, a quality mark; 3, the maker's mark, and 4, a date letter. The latter is useful for accurately dating antique watch cases. The Goldsmiths Company, London, marked gold cases from about 1685 and silver ones from about 1740. However, casemakers, although not members of the Goldsmiths Company, often struck their initials on cases from 1680 on.

Hammer, Striking   Hammer to strike a clock, bell, or GONG. Early ones were operated by AUTOMATA. The first for 'BIG BEN'

87

weighed 8 cwt. and cracked the bell. Hammers of present domestic striking and chiming clocks have leather or plastic ends to improve the note. They are operated by a BARREL with cams or pins which press on the tails of the hammers to lift and release them.

Hampton Court Clock Large ASTRONOMICAL CLOCK made *c.* 1540, at Hampton Court Palace, Middlesex.

Hand, Clock Until about 1400 a clock had a rotating dial and a fixed hand. The first moving (hour) hands were like short arrows, with a pointed tail to make it easier to set them by hand. The arrow head on LANTERN CLOCKS later became heart shaped, then for LONG CASE CLOCKS it was pierced and elaborated. The minute hand came into general use after mid-seven-

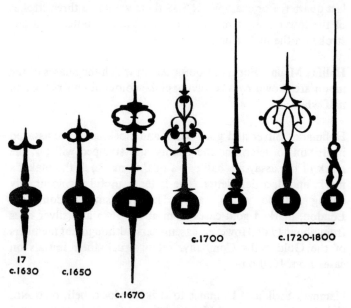

Fig. 14. Clock hands.

teenth century and seconds hands became popular after 1660 when the long case clock came into use, the first of these having no tails. Both minute and seconds hands are, however, found on some very early special clocks (*see* **Dondi's Clock**). The finest hands were pierced and carved by hand and blued by heat, the hour and minute hands being considerably contrasted. Now clock hands are stamped out and coloured chemically, often having too little contrast between hour and minute. Hands of big public clocks were made of copper and bronze and are now often of aluminium alloy.

Hand, Watch Before about 1700 watches had one thick hour hand, which was adjusted by pushing it. The accuracy of the HAIRSPRING encouraged the addition of a minute hand, and that of the CYLINDER ESCAPEMENT, a seconds hand. Early English hands were 'beetle' (like a stag-beetle) for the hour and 'poker' for the minute. French ones were often pierced. A modern fine steel or gold hand requires over 20 manufacturing operations.

Hanging Clock Weight-driven clock that is hung from the wall, such as a LANTERN or a HOODED CLOCK.

Hard Gold Plating A method of plating watch cases with a gold alloy that can be hardened by heat treatment to make it more durable.

Harrison, John (1693–1776) Self-taught son of a carpenter from Foulby, Yorkshire, who, with his brother James, made extremely accurate clocks with wooden wheels (to avoid oiling). When the British Government offered a £20,000 prize for 'solving' or FINDING THE LONGITUDE to help ships' navigation, he devoted the rest of his life to this, visiting London with his ideas, where GRAHAM lent him money. During the next six years he built his No. 1 timekeeper, which showed seconds, minutes, hours, and days, and worked very well on a sea voyage to Lisbon on test. Eventually his No. 4, a big watch, qualified for the prize by being only 15 seconds slow after five months at sea. The BOARD OF LONGITUDE refused to pay him fully and it was only after many years of dispute and the intervention of the King, that Parliament overruled the Board, and Harrison received the remaining money, at the age of 80! Invented GRIDIRON compensation, the GRASSHOPPER ESCAPEMENT, TEMPERATURE COMPENSATION, and a form of MAINTAINING POWER. Worked in later years in Red Lion Square, London. Buried in Hampstead churchyard.

Hatton Garden   Traditional home of the diamond merchants in London and once the garden of Ely House. Now also a centre of much of the clock and watch trade, which moved from CLERKENWELL.

Helical Spring   Another name for a CYLINDRICAL SPRING.

Hemicyclium   Sundial shaped like quarter of a sphere and thought to have been invented by Berosus, the Chaldean astronomer, about 300 B.C. There is one at Pompeii.

Henlein, Peter   German clockmaker traditionally supposed to have invented the MAINSPRING for clocks and thus made the first portable clock or watch about 1510 (*see* **Nurnberg Egg**). It is more likely that the first watches were made in Italy before 1488.

Highest Church Clock   In England, this is in Limehouse Parish Church, with 200 steps to the clock room.

Hog's Bristle   *See* **Bristle Regulator.**

Hood   The top of a LONG CASE CLOCK case enclosing the MOVEMENT. The hood was lifted up for removal—and called a 'rising hood'—until about 1685, after which it was pulled forwards.

Hooded Clock Transitional clock between the LANTERN and the LONG CASE, the lantern clock being partly enclosed by a wooden HOOD, but still being hung on the wall.

Hooke, Robert (1635–1703) An eccentric genius, first experimenter of The Royal Society, horological inventor, and pioneer of the microscope. Discovered the law of springs (*see* **Anagram**). Invented various HAIRSPRINGS in 1664 which may have included a spiral one. In answer to HUYGENS' claim, he declared 'Zulichem's spring not worth a farthing!' Designed a toothed wheel-cutting engine for clockmakers in 1670. Dr Hooke may have invented the ANCHOR ESCAPEMENT made by CLEMENT. Collaborated closely with TOMPION.

Hooke's Law The law of springs discovered by Dr HOOKE which states that the force produced by a spring is proportional to its tension. *See* **Anagram.**

Horizontal Escapement Alternative name for the CYLINDER ESCAPEMENT, because the ESCAPE WHEEL was parallel to the other wheels and not at right angles to them, as in the VERGE.

Horloge Name given to both water and mechanical clocks in the Middle Ages, which makes it difficult to decide which is meant in ancient manuscripts.

Horology The study of time and timekeeping.

Hour Twenty-fourth part of a day, equivalent to 15° of rotation of the Earth. Hours were often of variable length (*see* **Canonical Hours, Temporal Hours** *and* **Japanese Clock**). The division of 24 may have come about as described under

91

MINUTE. An hour is now based on the definition of one SECOND. The Italians were probably the first to use the 24-hour system (as opposed to two 12's) from the fourteenth century.

Hour-Glass   A SAND-GLASS arranged to time an hour's interval.

House Clock   Early name for a domestic or CHAMBER CLOCK, when there was usually only one in the home.

Huaud   Three Geneva painters, Pierre, Jean, and Amy Huaud became famous for ENAMELLED WATCHES, from about 1679.

Human Clock   Habits of all living organisms, including man, obey built-in 'clocks' with solar-daily, lunar-daily, monthly, and annual rhythms, e.g. the growth of a potato and the colour changes of a fiddler crab both have daily cycles depending on the moon. An interesting fact is that a human clock can be stopped (e.g. by freezing) and restarted, and can be reset, but cannot be speeded up or slowed down.

Hunter   Normally a pocket watch with a hinged lid over the face, but wrist-watches are occasionally made hunter style. A half-hunter has a hole in the centre of the lid to read the time —supposedly Napoleon's idea.

Huygens, Christiaan (1629–95)   Dutch scientist who invented the first practical PENDULUM clock in 1657, which was made for him by Salomon Coster; discovered CIRCULAR ERROR; and wrote the first accurate treatise on the pendulum, 'HOROLOGIUM OSCILLATORIUM'. Handsome and gifted man who was given an English title. Probable inventor of the spiral BALANCE SPRING, 1675 (*but see* **Hooke**). Often referred to as 'Zulichem'. (*See* Plate 2.)

Ilbert Collection   One of the most famous collections of clocks, watches, other timekeepers, and books ever amassed, by C. A. Ilbert (1888–1956). The clocks were bought for the nation by an anonymous donor, and the watches by public appeal and donations, through the efforts of the CLOCKMAKERS COMPANY. They are now in the BRITISH MUSEUM.

Ilbert Library   Famous library of horological books left by C. A. Ilbert in 1957 to the BRITISH HOROLOGICAL INSTITUTE.

Impulse   The small force applied at intervals to a PENDULUM or BALANCE to keep it swinging.

Impulse Pin   Small pin by which IMPULSE is given to a BALANCE. *See* **Ruby Pin** *and* Fig. 17.

Impulse Dial   Another name for a SLAVE DIAL.

Independent Seconds   Clock or watch with seconds hand—today usually a CENTRE SECONDS HAND—which jumps from one second to the next, i.e. it is DEAD BEAT, also called 'jump second'. BREGUET invented a jumping hour hand.

Index   A watch REGULATOR which effectively alters the length of the HAIRSPRING for final timekeeping adjustments. The outer end of the spring is fixed and the index, which is a lever, moves two CURB PINS (one each side of the spring) around a short arc of the spring from this point.   *See illustration overleaf.*

Ingold, Pierre-Frederic (1787–1878)   Pioneer of mechanized watchmaking from Bienne, who worked for BREGUET in Paris, introduced JEWELS to Switzerland, entered negotiations with the JAPYS, but could not agree and tried to set up a watch-making factory in France. He transferred to London, where his Soho factory was damaged by hand-made watch workers, so moved to the U.S.A. and became a U.S. citizen. There his ideas were adopted and the first factories set up in Boston, but he personally was expelled without reason. He returned to La

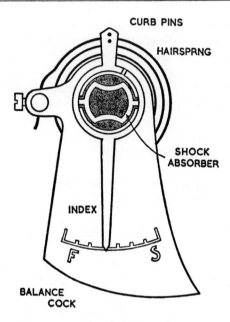

Fig. 15. Index.

Chaux de Fonds and tried again unsuccessfully to set up a factory, dying there at the age of 92. In the meantime watch-making by machinery had been started by Leschot in Geneva. Ingold drills were used until recently.

Inro Watch The Japanese used to carry medicines in small decorated wooden boxes called an 'inros'. In the eighteenth century many of these were converted to watches. They were worn attached by cords, and a button (the 'netsuke'), to the kimono belt. There is a small drawer in the inro for the watch key.

Interval Timer Clock mechanism that can be set to a given time interval and rings a bell or turns a switch at the end of it,

(above) Miniature BRACKET CLOCK by the famous English maker, Thomas TOMPION. The cords are for the PULL REPEATER. (left) Swiss MINIATURE WATCH with its winding key, shown with a sixpence.

PLATE 1

(right) A LONG CASE clock by George GRAHAM with the MERCURIAL PENDULUM he invented in 1721. It has a BREAK ARCH DIAL.

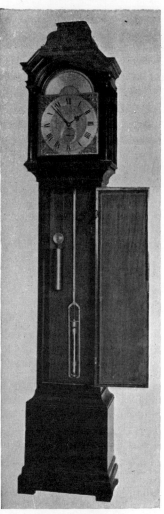

(left) The first PENDULUM CLOCK, invented by Christiaan HUYGENS and made in 1657. The bottom wheel is a GOING BARREL, the centre one a CONTRATE WHEEL, and the top one with sharp teeth a CROWN WHEEL.

PLATE 2

(above) The earliest clock still working, in SALISBURY Cathedral, Wiltshire. It has a restored VERGE and FOLIOT ESCAPEMENT and was made in 1386.

(above) A BALL CLOCK by Radeloff, *c.* 1651. The ball drives the clock, which has a CROSS-BEAT ESCAPEMENT.

(below) An early DRUM TABLE CLOCK with its original leather case.

PLATE 3

(above) JAPANESE CLOCK in which the hour numerals can be moved.

(above) A FORM WATCH of CRUCIFORM shape. The 'glass' is rock crystal.

(below) Front dial of a Le Roy watch of 1896 said to be the most COMPLICATED WATCH in the world.

(below) A MAIL GUARD'S WATCH.

PLATE 4

(above) A watch of so-called PURITAN style, with one hand, by Edward EAST, made about 1640.

(above) German CHAMBER CLOCK made of iron, about 1570, with striking, chiming, alarm and MOON DIAL.

(right) American WAGGON SPRING clock. The driving spring can be seen at the bottom.

PLATE 5

(above) ROLLING CLOCK of about 1665 in the Dresdener Zwinger Museum.

(above) French MONTH CLOCK with SKELETON frame. *c.* 1760.

Photo: Courtesy of F. B. Royer-Collard

(below) CONGREVE CLOCK in which a rolling ball is the timekeeper.

PLATE 6

(above) On the left is a silver English watch of *c*. 1650 with its PINWORK PAIR CASE. And on the right a watch with WANDERING HOUR DIAL.

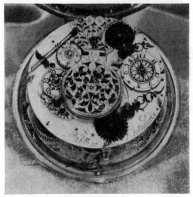

(right) Back of a big striking TRAVELLING WATCH *c*. 1690. The numbered dial on the left is the REGULATOR and that on the right the LOCKING PLATE.

(below) Two views of the Accutron ELECTRONIC WATCH movement.

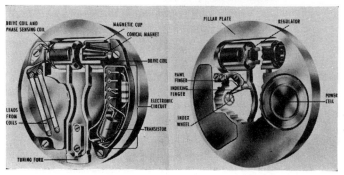

PLATE 7

(left) RING WATCH of the nineteenth century set with pearls. It also has an automatic calendar!

(right) An AUTOMATON watch. The gold cupids on the dial work a see-saw.

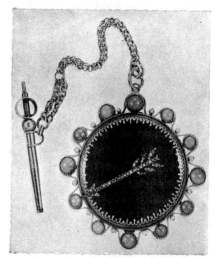

(left) BLIND MAN'S WATCH of 1810. The diamond arrow on the enamelled cover is turned until it stops. The feel of the arrow against the turquoise beads gives the time. That shown is 8 o'clock.

PLATE 8

such as a kitchen, PROCESS, TELEPHONE, or PHOTOGRAPHIC TIMER.

Invar   Alloy of 35.6% nickel with the remainder steel, invented by GUILLAUME and named from '*invar*iable' as its expansion at different temperatures is negligible. Invar PENDULUM rods solve TEMPERATURE COMPENSATION problems. *See* **Compensation Pendulum.**

Inverted Escapement   Arrangement with the ANCHOR under the ESCAPE WHEEL instead of on top. The first OBSERVATORY CLOCKS by TOMPION has this; so have some earlier American clocks.

Iron Clock   First domestic clocks (in Italy, Germany, and France), early public clocks and watches too, were made of wrought iron because their makers—blacksmiths and lock-smiths—worked in this metal. BRASS was introduced in the sixteenth century on the Continent for cases and dials and spread to England at the beginning of the seventeenth century although used in the fourteenth for DONDI'S CLOCK.

Isochronism   Occupying equal time. Used of a BALANCE or PENDULUM when the time of swing does not vary whatever the arc of swing. Almost impossible to achieve in practice (although some MARINE CHRONOMETERS approach it) thus resulting in POSITIONAL ERRORS in watches. *See* **Circular Error, Galileo** *and* **Airy.**

Italian Horological Industry   There is paper evidence of the world's first watches being made in Italy before 1488. Mantua was an important centre in the fifteenth century. The earliest ALARM clock in existence is also Italian, an interesting fact being that it is made of brass. The Italians eventually lost the lead to the French, Germans, and English. Clocks of many types including alarms and tower clocks and some watches are made today.

Italian Hours   Early Italian method of dividing EQUAL HOURS into one series numbered from 1 to 24, starting at every sunset. DONDI'S CLOCK employed this system.

Jack   Originally a man struck the CANONICAL HOURS on a bell when a small ALARM warned him to do so. Then a mechanical man (AUTOMATON) was invented to strike the bell, one of the earliest known being called 'Jacquemard' (Jack o' the clock), in 1517 records of the 1383 clock of Dijon, France. This became contracted to 'Jack' in England, as with JACK BLANDIFER.

Jack Blandifer   Name of fourteenth century mechanical figure or JACK that sits above an arch inside Wells Cathedral. He strikes the hours on a bell with a hammer in one hand, nods his head, and sounds the quarters by kicking other bells with his heels. *See* **Wells Clock.**

Jack the Smiter   Clock JACK at Southwold, Suffolk, in fifteenth-century 'armour', now operated by a rope.

Japanese Clock   Dutch traders took VERGE and FOLIOT clocks to Japan in 1600. The Japanese copied these, but did not follow European trends. Instead, they adapted clocks to show Japanese hours. Until as late as 1873, a day was divided into six night hours and six day hours. Since periods of daylight altered through the year, so did the lengths of both day and night hours. Clocks were therefore made to go one RATE in the day and another at night, by using two foliots. Hour divisions could be adjusted by hand, or dials replaced by others at each month. Each six hour period was numbered backwards 9, 8, 7, 6, 5, and 4, starting from 12 noon and midnight. Striking followed suit. Clocks of the period striking half hours sound them alternatively with single and double blows. So a Japanese clock of the period strikes 9 at 12 noon; 1 at 12.30 p.m.; 8 at 1 p.m.; 2 at 1.30 p.m.; 7 at 2 p.m.; 1 at 2.30 p.m., and so on.

Collectors divide old Japanese clocks into three varieties: 'LANTERN', 'BRACKET' (Plate 4) (introduced in the nineteenth century), and 'pillar', a type not found elsewhere. On a pillar clock a pointer indicates the time on a straight, vertical scale, which is changed monthly.

Japanese Horological Industry The modern industry in Japan has grown rapidly since the Second World War and produces many forms of clock and watch, including JEWELLED LEVERS. Its watch output is about 4 % of the world total, and it was one of the first to produce a QUARTZ CRYSTAL domestic clock. American companies have a stake in the industry.

Japy, Frederic (1749–1812) Swiss inventor of the earliest machine tools for making watches, particularly of LEPINE CALIBRE design. Pioneer of the FRENCH HOROLOGICAL INDUSTRY.

Jeanrichard, Daniel Went to Le Locle in Switzerland in 1700 and, with his five sons, became a pioneer of watchmaking in the Neuchatel area, particularly by factory methods. There is a statue of him in Le Locle.

Jens Olsen's Clock Magnificent ASTRONOMICAL CLOCK, which is probably the most accurate ever made. Erected in Copenhagen City Hall, made by Jens Olsen during 1944–55, and subscribed to by every member of the Danish nation as a symbol of delivery from the German occupation.

Jesuit Clocks Striking clocks introduced into China by Jesuit missionaries after 1585.

Jewel Clock or watch bearing made of synthetic ruby, comprising a ring (the 'hole') with a SINK for oil. Invented in 1704 by Nicholas Facio, and Peter and Jacob Debaufre, who used pierced natural rubies. Many other gemstones have been used including garnet (which is too soft) and diamond. Now synthetic ruby or sapphire is universal. Also an END STONE to take the end thrust of a pivot, an IMPULSE PIN, and a PALLET made of synthetic ruby for watches or agate for clocks. Jewels reduce friction and wear. Making them is a highly specialized separate industry. A court case in 1962 established that it is illegal in the U.K. to advertise or sell watches by 'jewels' that are not truly functional. A non-AUTOMATIC WATCH with 15 jewels is considered fully jewelled. Large numbers, particularly as high as 41, 56, and 77, should be suspect. *See* **Shock Absorber** (Figs. 17 *and* 24).

Jewelled Lever   A watch of better quality, with a LEVER ESCAPEMENT which has jewelled PALLETS, not PIN PALLETS.

Jockele Clock   Small BLACK FOREST CLOCK, named after those about 3 in. high made *c.* 1780 by 'Jockele' Herbstrieth.

Journeyman   After seven years, an APPRENTICE clockmaker had to work as a journeyman for two years, before he was allowed to submit his MASTERPIECE to the CLOCKMAKERS COMPANY. If the masterpiece was approved, he was granted Freedom of the Company and could become a MASTER clockmaker. Apprentices lived on the premises but journeymen could live out, i.e. they 'journeyed' to work.

Jumping Dial   Clock or watch dial with DIGITAL RECORDING on which the numerals are seen through apertures, the hours 'jumping' or changing every hour and the minutes every minute. Such watches go in and out of fashion. Also employed in small public clocks. A variation is the TICKET CLOCK.

Karrusel   Arrangement similar to the TOURBILLON in which the ESCAPEMENT revolves every $52\frac{1}{2}$ minutes; invented by Aarne Bonniksen in Coventry in 1894.

Kassel   Ancient centre of clockmaking where BURGI and others worked. Some fine ASTRONOMICAL CLOCKS are preserved in the State Museum. Kassel is in Hessen, Germany.

Kew 'A' Certificate   Performance certificate for timekeepers introduced in 1885 at the Kew Observatory, Old Deer Park, Richmond, and taken over by the NATIONAL PHYSICAL LABORA-TORY at Teddington, in 1912. This, and the lower grade 'B' Certificate tests, were superseded in 1951 by the N.P.L. CRAFTSMANSHIP TEST. The Kew Observatory was originally built for King George III who was keenly interested in time-keepers. Now it is the Air Ministry Meteorological Office. *See* **Rating Certificate** *and* **Timekeeping Trials.**

Key   Used for winding, or sometimes for SETTING UP, the MAINSPRING. No watch keys before the seventeenth century have survived. The early crank type in iron or brass was replaced by the T-shaped key around 1650, which became elaborately pierced and engraved or set with agate, rock crystal, or cameos after the Commonwealth. The best watches had gold or silver keys from about 1680 to 1770. At about this time, simpler brass and steel keys were introduced, but London makers still supplied gilt embossed crank keys with watches for the Turkish market until around 1840. Clock keys were similar but not so decorative. Many spring-driven clocks today have their keys permanently attached.

Keyless Watch   Having to wind a watch by a separate KEY was a nuisance as the key was easily lost. In the eighteenth century many attempts were made to invent keyless winding but it was not until 1820 that T. Prest, foreman to J. R. ARNOLD produced a successful winding button. The mechanism in modern watches was invented by Adrien Phillipe in 1843 and developed by Le Coultre and Audemars.

99

Kitchen Clock   Normally a wall clock for kitchen use.

Knibb, Joseph (b. 1640)   Joseph and his younger brother John became renowned clockmakers. Joseph is recorded as 'gardner' to Trinity College, Oxford, as well as a clockmaker. Later he set up at 'The Dial' in Fleet Street, London. He used ROMAN STRIKING and also made NIGHT CLOCKS. John remained in Oxford and was Mayor in 1700.

Lacquered Case   Wooden clock case finish for which the painter employed powder and lacquer to produce raised, coloured patterns. Popular from about 1700 to 1730 for LONG CASE CLOCKS, and still enjoying some vogue for small clocks today. Also called 'japanned case'.

Lacquering   Exposed brass parts of clocks and MARINE CHRONOMETERS are usually given a coat of clear lacquer to avoid discoloration and corrosion. A LACQUERED CASE has a different process applied to it.

Lamp Clock   Early timekeeper comprising a lamp with a glass reservoir scaled to indicate time as the oil burned away. *See* **Candle Clock.**

Lancet Clock   Wooden-cased clock, shaped like a Gothic arch, made during the first part of the nineteenth century after the period of hand-made clocks.

Lantern Clock   Form of clock with lantern-shaped brass case made in England for about a century after 1630 or so. Most had one hand; all were weight-driven with a bell on top and stood on a wall bracket. The first had BALANCES without springs and later ones had PENDULUMS.

100

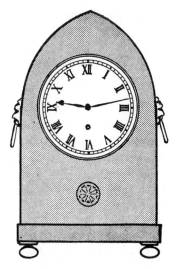

Fig. 16. Lancet clock.

Lantern Pinion Earliest form of gear, like a squirrel cage, or cylinder, made up of rods fitting into disc ends. Still used in some American alarm clocks. *See* **Pinion.**

Leaf Clockmaker's name for a tooth of the small driven gear wheel called a 'PINION'.

Left-Handed Watch Swiss wrist-watch with winding button on opposite 9 instead of 3 and regulated for wearing on the outside of the right wrist.

Lepine Calibre In the eighteenth century, all watches had their BALANCES outside the two circular PLATES that comprised the watch FRAME. About 1770, Antoine Lepine began making watches with one plate and a number of COCKS or BRIDGES, the balance being within the frame. This made the construction much thinner and heralded the modern watch. French makers

101

adopted this style, but English continued with the old ideas for about a century.

Le Roy, Julien (1686–1759)   Most famous French maker, particularly of REPEATER watches. Horologer du Roi. Perfected the OIL SINK about 1725 and may have invented the rod GONG and DUMB REPEATER. Often used the CYLINDER ESCAPEMENT designed by GRAHAM. His son Pierre (1717–85), also Horologer du Roi, became as famous, particularly for MARINE CHRONO-METERS, his finest (now in the Musée des Arts et Métiers, Paris) having one of the first DETACHED ESCAPEMENTS, a temperature COMPENSATED BALANCE and ISOCHRONOUS hairspring. This had more future influence on marine chronometers even than HARRISON's. *See* **Sully.**

Lever Escapement   The most successful of all ESCAPEMENTS, invented by Thos. Mudge in 1759 for QUEEN CHARLOTTE's WATCH, and improved by Josiah Emery, in 1785, who added DRAW. Now used in almost all watches and PLATFORM ESCAPE-MENT clocks, in conjunction with a BALANCE WHEEL and HAIR-SPRING. Also called 'detached lever' because of the freedom of the balance. Capable of high timekeeping performance. From Fig. 17, the balance swings clockwise and the RUBY PIN on it enters the lever fork, moving the lever upwards. This releases the ESCAPE WHEEL tooth marked A, which moves across the exit PALLET stone, pushing it right. This IMPULSES the balance in the same direction as it is swinging by causing the lever fork to thrust on the ruby pin. The escape wheel is stopped from turning further (under the influence of the MAINSPRING) by tooth B coming against the side of the entrance pallet. On the return swing of the balance (under the influence of the HAIR-SPRING), the lever is knocked the other way and the balance impulsed anti-clockwise by tooth B acting on the entrance pallet. Called 'anchor' on the Continent owing to its similarity to the ANCHOR ESCAPEMENT.

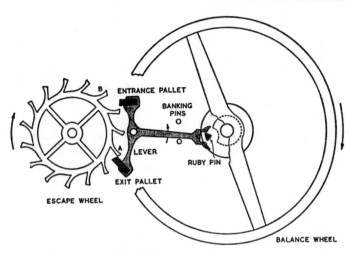

Fig. 17. Lever escapement.

Lever Watch   Loose term meaning a watch which has a LEVER ESCAPEMENT with jewelled PALLETS, although a PIN PALLET watch is also a lever.

Light Clock   Modern Swiss clock by Patek Philippe which is wound by the action of light on a photo-electric cell, the small current produced turning a motor which winds the MAINSPRING. The mainspring gives a reserve of power for the darkness and the clock therefore never needs to be wound.

Lightfoot, Peter   Traditional maker of fourteenth century elaborate clock at Glastonbury Abbey and WELLS CATHEDRAL CLOCK. Both Wells and SALISBURY clocks were more likely made by a Johannes Lietuyt of Delft, Holland, for Bishop Erghum. But Lightfoot may have been a contraction of 'Lietuyt'. *See* **British Horological Industry.**

Lighthouse Clock   Tall table clock shaped like a lighthouse

103

with a clock dial in the tower. Where the lamphouse would be is a cylinder made up of glass prisms, which rotates. In one version the 'lamphouse' is actually a TORSION PENDULUM controlling the clock. Made in France in the nineteenth century. Another form has a rotating clock dial in the top under a glass dome.

Ligne Watchmaker's measure equal to about 1/11th inch, or 2.26 mm. Originated in France as 1/12th pouce, or French inch. Commonly used today, as in a '10 ligne MOVEMENT', but slowly being replaced by millimetres. In the past, lignes differed in various countries; there was an English line, and 12 of them or 3 barleycorns made an inch. *See* **Size.**

Limoges Enamel Painted opaque enamel decoration for watch cases from 1500–1600. *See* **Enamelled Watch.**

Local Time Time in a particular place or area. This was SOLAR TIME when timekeeping was by SUNDIAL. It became mean solar time after clocks came into general use. Now it normally means STANDARD TIME.

Locking The action of an ESCAPEMENT when it 'locks' or holds up a tooth of the ESCAPE WHEEL.

Locking Plate Early form of COUNT WHEEL, or in modern parlance 'memory', for STRIKING clocks. Notches in the rim decide how many hammer blows the striking TRAIN will give after being released at the hour. Really a misnomer. Gradually superseded by RACK STRIKING after 1676. Most locking plates are outside the BACK PLATE of a clock, but some early ones were between the plates. Locking plate striking can become out of step with the time shown, but is easily set right by releasing the striking train without touching the hands until the two agree (Plate 7).

London Museum Collection   European sixteenth to eighteenth century clocks with some fine early German examples, at Kensington Palace, London.

Long Case Clock   Clock in a wooden case usually over 6 ft. tall standing on the floor. The MOVEMENT usually runs for 30 hours or for eight days, has a long PENDULUM ticking seconds, strikes the hours and sometimes the quarters also, and often has a CALENDAR DIAL, sometimes a MOON DIAL, and even a TIDAL DIAL. The first were introduced in England before 1660, probably originating from casings put around the weights of HANGING CLOCKS. They were also made in Holland, where the pendulum clock was invented. In the seventeenth and eighteenth centuries, they were made in large numbers; even the makers numbering tens of thousands. Most best makers went to London to work, but Edinburgh was another centre. CASES were often of oak with an ebony, walnut, or mahogany veneer. London set the style; country makers were slow to follow. DIALS of the best clocks were of brass, silvered on the CHAPTER RING bearing the engraved numbers. After about 1790, painted iron dials appeared, cases became uglier, and movements were quantity produced. In the nineteenth century mass-produced MANTEL CLOCKS superseded them. Another seventeenth-century name was 'coffin clock'; the name GRANDFATHER CLOCK did not become popular until much later (Plate 2).

Long Pendulum   A PENDULUM that swings from one side to the other in one or more seconds and is therefore a metre or more in length (*see* **Seconds Pendulum** *and* **Two-Seconds Pendulum**). The RYE CHURCH CLOCK has a BEAT of $2\frac{1}{4}$ sec. approx. So do the St Peter and St Paul Deddington, Oxon., and the Ringwood, Hants, church clocks. St Peter's Church at St Albans; Retford, Notts; and Antrim Parish Church, Northern Ireland, clocks have $2\frac{1}{2}$ sec. approx. pendulums. There are 3-sec. pendulums (about 29 ft. 4 in. long) on the clocks of

Churchill Church, Oxon., and Lewknor Church, Oxon., and a 4-sec. pendulum (approx. 52 ft. 2 in. long) on St Chad's Church clock, Shrewsbury.

Longitude   The angular distance east or west from longitude zero through GREENWICH OBSERVATORY, on which LOCAL and STANDARD TIMES, and NAVIGATION depend.

Lug   Shaped part of a watch CASE to which the strap or bracelet is attached.

Luminous Dial   The most successful means of making watches and clocks (particularly alarms) suitable for night use is to luminize the hands and dials. First applied in the U.S.A. at the beginning of the twentieth century, when the dangers were not understood and those who licked their paint brushes eventually died from radiation illness. There is no danger of radiation to the user, from properly luminized dials. The four million odd luminous watches and ten million luminous alarms in Britain give only one-hundredth of the natural background radiation from the Earth and outer space that no one can avoid. Luminous paint is a mixture of phosphor and a tiny amount of radium. The phosphor transforms the invisible radio-active rays from the radium into visible light. On good watches there are only thin fillings of luminous paint in the hands and small dots on the dial. Some have the paint under the hands. The colour of the glow is often made green because the eye is most sensitive to this colour. Some modern British SYNCHRONOUS alarms have electro-luminescent dials, the tension of electricity producing a glow without radiation.

Lund Cathedral Clock   Fine large astronomical clock with AUTOMATA in Lund, Sweden, the original going back to 1380.

Lyre Clock Elegant mantel clock inspired by the stringed instrument and invented by Kinable, of Paris (d. 1825). A fine one by him is in the VICTORIA AND ALBERT MUSEUM COLLECTION. The curved frame of the 'lyre' is of marble or bronze with the clock dial near the bottom. A GRIDIRON PENDULUM *above* the clock (suggesting the strings) is connected through its BOB to the clock ESCAPEMENT. Copied in large numbers in the U.S.A. after the Civil War.

Magic Lantern Clock Form of NIGHT CLOCK that projects an image of the dial on the wall. Invented in France in the eighteenth century and made in the nineteenth in various styles projecting the image from the front or back of the clock. The idea was revived in the twentieth century when electric clocks were made to project the dial and hands on the ceiling.

Magnet The idea of using a magnet instead of a BALANCE SPRING was invented as early as 1659 by Adam Kochanski. Special extremely powerful and tiny magnets are used in ELECTRIC and ELECTRONIC WATCHES, but these are to give IMPULSE by interaction with electro-magnets.

Magnetic Clock *See* **Tortoise Clock.**

Magnetic Escapement Invented by C. F. Clifford in England in 1948, this ESCAPEMENT has no physical contact between ESCAPE WHEEL and controlling element. Friction is extremely low and the action is silent. Used for German clocks and British TIME SWITCHES. The control element is a short length of spring which vibrates. On the end of this is a small horseshoe magnet. The specially shaped escape wheel teeth pass between the poles of the magnet which release them one by one as the magnet moves up and down.

Magnetic Suspension   A BALANCE WHEEL for modern clocks which carries a small ring magnet under it. This is oppositely magnetized to a fixed ring magnet around the lower PIVOT so that the balance assembly 'skates' on a magnetic field, considerably reducing friction. Another version uses a magnet a short distance above the steel balance STAFF (axle) to lift it and reduce friction.

Magnetism   Steel parts of watches, especially the HAIRSPRING if of steel, can become magnetized from TV circuits, magnetic kitchen and tool racks, generators, radar equipment, etc., and behave erratically. They can usually be demagnetized without difficulty. 'Anti-magnetic' watches are partly protected by having vital parts NON-MAGNETIC. The best protection is an anti-magnetic screen around the MOVEMENTS of special watches. ELECTRIC WATCHES can be affected and also demagnetized. The DEMAGNETIZER is not strong enough to damage the magnets in them.

Mail Guard's Watch   Special 'watch' carried by the guard on a mail coach, along with his blunderbuss, in the days before railways. Usually in a rectangular brass and wooden case which was locked at the depot. The guard was responsible to the company for seeing that the mail coach kept to its time schedule (Plate 4).

Mainspring   Coiled flat spring for driving a clock or watch, inventor unknown, but may have been a swordmaker/clockmaker of about 1450. The mainspring made the portable clock and the watch possible. Early springs were hammered out of steel or brass. They gave much more power wound than partly wound, which affected timekeeping. Attempts were made to compensate for this by STOPWORK, the STACKFREED, forms of FLY, and particularly the FUSEE. Modern springs are made of tempered carbon steel, stainless steel and various alloys; the unbreakable mainspring (for watches) is an alloy steel containing iron, carbon, nickel, chromium, cobalt, molybdenum, manganese, and beryllium. It is non-magnetic and was introduced in 1947. Some springs are set to a reversed curve like a figure 8 when free. Such alloy springs give more power as they age, not less, like steel springs. Power output of modern mainsprings is fairly even at different tensions, which improves timekeeping performance. Mainsprings break through fatigue, no lubrication, and sudden changes of temperature (*see* **Going Barrel** *and* **Setting Up**). One form of mainspring for modern clocks running a month at a winding and for ciné cameras is coiled round a free-running ARBOR when unstressed. It is wound in the opposite direction round an adjacent arbor. It then runs back onto the first, giving very even power output, but not MAINTAINING POWER, like a GOING BARREL.

Maintaining Power   A clock without a GOING BARREL loses time while it is being wound because there is temporarily no power to drive it. Maintaining work provides this power during winding by an extra weight or spring. A HUYGENS ENDLESS CHAIN in 30-hr. grandfather clocks and AUTOMATIC CLOCK WINDING in tower clocks automatically provides maintaining power. Some of the best weight-driven LONG CASE CLOCKS have BOLT-AND-SHUTTER maintaining power. A similar arrangement for tower clocks is a weighted lever which has to be moved before the winding handle can be turned. Moving it applies power to a clock wheel through a ratchet. For FUSEE clocks and watches, and MARINE CHRONOMETERS, a spring-driven maintaining power invented by John HARRISON in 1735 is employed.

Main Wheel   The driving first wheel in a clock or watch, usually attached to, or part of, the BARREL. In a FUSEE timepiece it is attached to the fusée and often called the 'great wheel'.

Mantel Clock   Clock intended to be placed on a mantelpiece; otherwise similar to a BRACKET CLOCK. The latest are made thin to suit mantels over electric and gas fires.

Marie Antoinette Watch   Celebrated masterpiece by BREGUET commissioned for the Queen by an officer of the French Royal Guard. It was constructed from 1783 to 1802, by which time the Queen had been executed. The watch incorporated every complication of the time. It was SELF WINDING, with a MINUTE REPEATER, PERPETUAL CALENDAR, INDEPENDENT SECONDS HAND, EQUATION OF TIME DIAL, UP-AND-DOWN DIAL, and a thermometer. The outer gold case was never finished.

Marine Chronometer   Special very accurate timekeeper with a DETENT ESCAPEMENT used for NAVIGATION at sea, surveying, and scientific purposes. Developed by LE ROY, ARNOLD, and EARNSHAW (*see also* **Harrison**). The chronometer is usually in a brass case fixed in gimbals in a wooden box some 8 in. square, and runs for two or eight days. It has a COMPENSATION BALANCE with a HELICAL SPRING driven from a MAINSPRING and FUSEE with MAINTAINING POWER. It also has an UP-AND-DOWN DIAL incorporated in its traditional form of dial. *See* **Deck Watch.**

Marine Clock   Spring-driven clock with PLATFORM ESCAPEMENT in a cylindrical brass case with a flange at the back for mounting on a bulkhead. For general use. The MARINE CHRONOMETER or DECK WATCH is more accurate for NAVIGATION.

Marquetry   Inlaid patterns of holly, boxwood, or ivory in walnut or ebony veneer, usually of LONG CASE CLOCKS. Some were in panels; some all over. Used from about 1675–1720. Superseded largely by burr walnut (*see* **Case, Clock**). BOULLE work is also a form of marquetry.

110

Mary Queen of Scots' Watch   Large SKULL WATCH believed to have been given by the Queen to Mary Seton, one of her Maids of Honour. The forehead of the skull is engraved with a figure of death between a palace and a cottage, and a quotation in Latin meaning 'pale death visits with impartial foot the cottages of the poor and the castles of the rich' (Horace). The skull is held upside down and the jaw lifted to read the silver dial. The hour is struck on a bell. Made by Moyant à Blois (1570–90). The escapement is unfortunately a CONVERSION to lever.

Mass Dial   Ancient sundial to remind churchgoers of times of service. Usually seen today as a little group of radiating lines marking the TIDES, scratched on the south porch of the church. Originally there was a rod sticking out from the centre.

Master   Clock or watchmaker who had served an APPRENTICE-SHIP and had his MASTERPIECE approved by the Court of the Worshipful Company of Clockmakers.

Master Clock   Clock which controls SLAVE DIALS, a TOWER CLOCK dial, or PROGRAMME CONTROLLER. Invented by Alexander Bain in 1840. Most modern electric master clocks have a SECONDS PENDULUM impulsed by a GRAVITY ARM. Each time it swings to the right, the pendulum turns a 30-toothed wheel one tooth. At each full turn (half minute), a lever on this wheel unlatches a gravity arm which gives an IMPULSE by pressing on an arm fixed to the pendulum. The gravity arm then drops on to an electric contact which operates an electro-magnet to reset the arm and also to provide a brief current to operate SLAVE DIALS.

Masterpiece   The special clock or watch that an APPRENTICE, after a period as a JOURNEYMAN, had to submit for approval (to the Worshipful Company of Clockmakers if he were English) before he could set up on his own. *See* **Clockmakers Company** *and* **Nurnberg.**

Matted Dial   Centres of brass antique clock dials were often given a rough matt surface by rolling them in all directions with a matting tool—a knurled and hardened, steel roller in a handle. This was done by hand. Today the finish is copied by acid etching.

Mean Time   Mean SOLAR TIME, the time shown by clocks. Days and hours shown by the SUNDIAL actually vary in length. When time was averaged into EQUAL HOURS, this was called 'mean time'.

Mercurial Pendulum   A form of TEMPERATURE COMPENSATION invented by George GRAHAM in 1721. The BOB of the pendulum is one or two jars of mercury. As the pendulum rod expands downwards in heat, the mercury expands upwards, thus keeping the effective length, or CENTRE OF OSCILLATION, the same. In the RIEFLER CLOCK, the rod of the pendulum is a steel tube almost filled with mercury, which gives better compensation because it is effective over the whole length of the pendulum (Plate 2).

Meridian   The highest position of the Sun in the sky, which indicates noon. Also the highest position of a star. The meridian of a particular place is a circle passing through it and the North and South Poles, i.e. its LONGITUDE.

Meridian Line   The line of longitude zero passing through GREENWICH OBSERVATORY from which GREENWICH MEAN TIME is measured. It is marked in the forecourt by a white line so that visitors can stand with one foot in the eastern and the other in the western hemisphere.

Metropolitan Museum Collection   Fine collection of timekeepers in New York, which includes the PIERPONT MORGAN COLLECTION of watches.

Microsecond   A millionth of a second, symbol μs.

Middle Temperature Error   A BI-METALLIC BALANCE and HAIR-SPRING is only truly accurate at two temperatures. In between these, the timepiece gains. This middle temperature error was reduced by AUXILIARY COMPENSATION (used particularly on MARINE CHRONOMETERS) and almost eliminated by the GUIL-LAUME BALANCE. Modern materials have eliminated it. *See* **Compensation Balance.**

Millisecond   Thousandth of a SECOND, contracted to 'ms'.

Miniature Rotor   A very small winding ROTOR, less than half the diameter of the SELF-WINDING WATCH, which enables the watch to be made thin.

Miniature Watch   *See* **Smallest Watch** *and* Plate 1.

Minute   Sixtieth part of an hour. The Babylonians divided the path of the Sun into 360 steps representing days of the year, which gave us our 360° in a circle. Since angles of 60° were easily constructed and the smallest division of 60 by repeated halving is 15, 360° was divided into 24 angles of 15°. As the Earth turns 360° in a day, the day was thus divided into 24 hours. The association of 60° with time may therefore account for the division of the hour into 60 minutes. (*But see* definition of **Second.**)

Minute Hand   Hand indicating minutes, incorporated as early as the sixteenth century on ASTRONOMICAL CLOCKS, but not in general use for clocks until after the practical PENDULUM was invented in 1657 and for watches until about 1700, after the BALANCE SPRING was invented.

113

Minute Repeater   A REPEATER WATCH or CLOCK that will sound the last hour, quarter, and minute on bells or gongs, at will. Such clocks were made from the early eighteenth century and watches from the nineteenth. The last hour is sounded first in the deeper of two tones, the last quarter is sounded by one, two, or three TING TANGS on the two gongs, then the number of minutes in the higher tone. The earliest known is by Benedict Felder.

Mock Pendulum   Some pendulum BRACKET CLOCKS have a curved slot near the top of the dial in which a disc (the mock pendulum) fixed to the PALLETS swings to and fro, to show the clock is going. Also called a 'false bob'. *See* **Pendulum Watch.**

MOCK PENDULUM

Fig. 18. Mock pendulum.

Momento Mori   Reminder of death. Another name for SKULL WATCH or clock.

Monastery Clock   Very early ALARM used in Monasteries to give warning to a monk of when to ring the prayer bell. Most still existing are of iron in GOTHIC style, but the earliest of them made in Italy in the fourteenth or fifteenth century is of brass with a 24-hour revolving dial and fixed hand, and a wheel type of BALANCE. It is only 9¾ in. high and is in a private collection in Italy. *See* **Canonical Hours.**

Monumental Clock   One built like a monument.

Moon Dial   Aperture behind which a dial is moved to show an engraved or painted moon face gradually wax and wane. Common on clocks from about 1750. The moon was then the only 'street lighting'. For most clocks, the lunar month is 29½ days (actually it is 29 days 12 hr. 44 min. 3 sec.). Two moon faces are shown, one black (new moon) and one white (full moon). Later clocks have two full moons, displayed one after the other, on a larger disc turned in 59 days in the BREAK ARCH. The age of the moon is often shown on the edge of the disc through a small aperture in the dial. Another form of moon dial is a globe painted half black and half white or silver which is revolved in a close-fitting hole in the dial by gearing during a lunation; sometimes called a 'Halifax Moon.'

Fig. 19. Moon dial.

Moon's Effect on Rate   In 1927–28, A. L. Loomis compared three FREE PENDULUM clocks with a QUARTZ CLOCK by means of a spark CHRONOGRAPH he invented. His results showed that during a lunar month the attraction of the moon on the pendulums caused them to vary by 2/10,000 of a second.

Morbier Clock French clock of unusual design, the early MOVEMENTS having bars instead of PLATES, and a straight instead of curved RACK to operate the striking. Usually LONG CASE or LANTERN style with a very wide and decorative LONG PENDULUM. Also called 'Comptoise clock'. Made in Morbier from about 1750 to this century. The style has changed.

Motion Work Twelve to one gearing driving the hour hand from the minute hand.

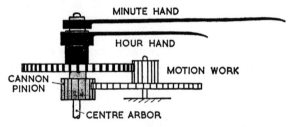

Fig. 20. Motion work.

Movement The 'works' of a timepiece.

Moving Arm Watch Watch in which a human figure (AUTO-MATON) on the dial indicates the time by moving its arms. The arm on the left points to the hour on a curved scale marked 12, 1, 2, 3 . . . 12; the other shows the minutes on a scale marked 0–60. Made in France in the nineteenth century. Also called 'bras mobile' or 'bras en l'air' watch.

Moving Eye Clock Animated figures with clocks include many with rolling eyes, the eyeballs being connected to the PENDULUM or BALANCE. Negroes, dogs, owls, and lions are examples.

Mozart This Austrian composer wrote some works in the eighteenth century for playing on musical clocks for Count Josef Deyn who had a collection. In *The Magic Flute*, he imitated mechanical music on bells.

Mudge, Thomas (1715–94) Made the greatest invention of all, the LEVER ESCAPEMENT, in QUEEN CHARLOTTE'S WATCH, 1759. He thought it capable of extremely good performance, but too complicated to be commercially successful. It was perfected 23 years later by Josiah Emery, who made three. Billions are in use today. Mudge also invented a REMONTOIRE and DETACHED ESCAPEMENT in a clock made for the Swiss astronomer Huber (who was once a pupil of the Astronomer Royal, Bradley) in 1755. Came from Exeter, was apprenticed to GRAHAM, in London, and became perhaps the finest craftsman of all. Left Fleet Street in 1771 to go to Plymouth and devote himself to perfecting MARINE CHRONOMETERS.

Musical Alarm An ALARM that plays a tune on a small MUSICAL BOX instead of ringing a bell. Produced in large numbers by the Swiss and Germans from 1897 to 1914 and still made.

Musical Box Clockwork mechanism playing music on bells or cymbals, or on the steel comb which may have been invented by Antide JANVIER in 1775. Louis Favre of Geneva probably made the first musical box in 1770. Musical movements were fitted into snuff-boxes, jewel cases, even watch and door keys. Best makers of larger musical boxes were Nicole Frères from 1815–1903. Most played six or eight tunes. Small musical movements are turned out by factories in Switzerland today in large quantities for musical cigarette boxes and other novelties.

Musical Clock Both TURRET CLOCKS and domestic clocks have been made to play tunes at the hour, one of the earliest of the latter by N. Vallin, 1598 (in the BRITISH MUSEUM COLLECTION), having 13 bells. Later ones had steel combs played by a revolving barrel with pins in it. Famous eighteenth-century makers were Robert Philip, Markwick Markham, David Evans, Wm. Carpenter, and Christopher PINCHBECK. Carillons of turret clocks are played by large revolving barrels operating the bell hammers. *See* **Organ Clock.**

Musical Watch   Watch playing a tune at the hour and usually at will also, by moving a slide. Invented about 1725 in Switzerland and most popular after 1800. The earliest had separate steel teeth, like the blades of a fan, plucked to give the notes by pins in a rotary disc. A metal comb and BARREL with pins superseded this. Some were REPEATERS, repeating the tune. *See* **Musical Box.**

Musk Ball Watch   Earliest form of watch still in existence. Those made by Peter HENLEIN were of this type. The case is a metal sphere about 4 in. in diameter. Like a scent 'bottle' of the period and, like it also, hung by chain or cord round the neck. The spring-driven MOVEMENT is inside the hinged case and the dial is a smaller diameter disc (like a base, for standing) at the bottom with one hand and no glass. Of the six such spherical watches known still to survive, the earliest is German and dated 1525–50. There is a German one of *c.* 1550 with CLOCK WATCH movement in the ASHMOLEAN MUSEUM; and a French one of 1551 by Jacques de la Garde in the NATIONAL MARITIME MUSEUM. The DRUM WATCH may have been invented about the same time or soon after. *See* **Nurnberg Egg.**

Mystery Clock   Clock which appears to work without any power or wheels. A domestic type has the hand 'floating' in double glass dial. Actually one of the circular glasses holds and rotates the hand, being driven from a MOVEMENT in the base. More mysterious are two large hands, freely attached to nothing but a sheet of glass, which work on their own. Each contains a watch movement in its counterpoise which alters the centre of gravity as it runs and causes the large hand to take up new positions. This idea was invented by John Schmidt, London, in 1808, who made clocks with an open CHAPTER RING and a single counterpoised hand, supported from the tail of a dolphin, and revolving without any apparent clockwork. Another mystery clock, invented by A. R. Guilmet, of Paris, in 1872, has a statuette on top of the case. In one hand, this figure holds a PENDULUM which swings without apparent connexion to the clock. Actually the statuette is given an almost imperceptible twist in alternate directions. IMPULSING is in principle similar to that in the RIEFLER CLOCK, through the SUSPENSION SPRING, 15 years later. There are examples in the VICTORIA AND ALBERT MUSEUM and ILBERT COLLECTIONS.

Nanosecond Thousand-millionth of a second. Used mainly for measuring electronic time intervals.

National Association of Watch and Clock Collectors Organization of collectors in the U.S.A. formed in 1943 to stimulate interest in studying and collecting timepieces. Publishes a bulletin and a 'mart', arranges meetings, has a library and a museum at the Franklyn Institute in Philadelphia, and 33 local chapters. Address: P.O. Box 33, Columbia, Pa., U.S.A.

National Maritime Museum Collection Fine examples of navigational timekeepers including HARRISON's, the world's second largest collection of ASTROLABES, and many other time-keeping instruments from SAND-GLASSES to TRANSIT INSTRU-MENTS, including the first French watch known. At Greenwich.

National Physical Laboratory Tests of timekeepers carried out at the Laboratory in Teddington, Middlesex, include the CRAFTSMAN TEST for watches, equivalent to Observatory tests in other countries; sporting tests for time of day CHRONOGRAPHS used for international sporting events; stop-watch and chronograph test; testing of stop-watches used for checking electricity meters; and chronometer test for survey and MARINE CHRONOMETERS. The ATOMIC CLOCK was developed by the N.P.L.

Nautical Almanac Astronomical tables giving star positions at different latitudes for every hour throughout the year, for NAVIGATION. Compiled by the ROYAL OBSERVATORY and published by H.M. Stationery Office. The title was changed to *Astronomical Ephemeris* in 1959, but other publishers still use the original name.

Navigation A navigator or surveyor can calculate his position north or south (latitude) by finding the height of the Sun or some other celestial body and referring to the NAUTICAL ALMANAC or AIR ALMANAC. Finding his position east or west (longitude) is complicated by the rotation of the Earth. LOCAL TIME becomes earlier west and later east of Greenwich. As the Earth revolves 360° in 24 hr., it moves 1° of longitude in 4 min. So if a sailor finds his local time is 5 hr. earlier than G.M.T. he is 75° west of Greenwich. To find local time he must know the date and take a 'fix' (find the position) of a star with a SEXTANT, in order to look up the local time in his almanac. G.M.T. is given by the ship's MARINE CHRONOMETER or RADIO TIME SIGNALS and must be accurate because an error of only 4 seconds equals one nautical mile. Most air navigation is done by special radio signals which fix the position of the aircraft at once. At other times the sailor's method is used, but by the time the position has been found the aircraft may have moved about 100 miles away from it.

Negro Clock Early German AUTOMATON clock with a ball-shaped clock on a post intended to look like a palm tree. Beside it stand a negro and a dog. The negro has a pointer which indicates the hour against a MOVING BAND around the ball. At the hour, the negro moves his head and the dog tries to jump.

Newsam, Bartholomew (d. 1593)   Clockmaker to Queen Elizabeth I after Nicolas Urseau. Worked in the Strand, having probably come from Yorkshire. Fine clock by him in the BRITISH MUSEUM.

Night Clock   The first known was by Johann Treffler and is in the KASSEL Museum Collection. As well as an ordinary dial for day, this has a glass dial with an oil lamp behind it. Another revolving glass dial carries a single hand. Clocks with illuminated hour numerals moving past a fixed point were common in Italy at the end of the seventeenth century. FROMANTEEL, EAST, and Joseph KNIBB made some in England. In these an oil lamp in the case shines through a perforated hour numeral, and marker hole above it, which moves during the hour round a large semi-circular slot in the dial. The slot is marked into four quarter hours and minutes for daytime use. At night, the time can be estimated to about five minutes by the position of the illuminated numeral. Night clocks had SILENT ESCAPEMENTS. Another type is the magic lantern clock. Current alarm clocks for night use have LUMINOUS dials, extra electric lamps, or are electro-luminescent, i.e. a glow of light is produced in the dial itself without bulbs by the tension of electricity.

Nivarox   A nickel-iron alloy with a little beryllium, invented by Carl Hass, Germany, as an improvement on ELINVAR for HAIRSPRINGS. By heat treatment during manufacture, its elasticity can be fixed at almost any value required. Thus it can be made to give any TEMPERATURE COMPENSATION desired, to eliminate temperature error in watches and clocks with balance wheels. It is non-magnetic, rustless, and tougher than steel. Other alloys with similar properties have been developed; they are Isoval, Durinval, and Nispan-C.

121

Nocturnal Instrument invented about 1520 for measuring the time at night. It is held at arm's length to sight the Pole Star. A lever is turned to line up the Great Bear constellation which appears to rotate once in 24 hours; thus the lever can indicate the time on a scale.

Non-Magnetic Fields of MAGNETISM have most effect on steel BALANCE WHEELS and HAIRSPRINGS. In the modern watch these are usually made of special alloys for TEMPERATURE COMPENSATION, which are also, fortunately, non-magnetic. Such watches are called 'non-magnetic' and are fairly resistant to magnetism, but not entirely as there are still steel parts that can be affected. Some special watches have a protective screen over the MOVEMENT inside the case. *See* **Demagnetizer.**

Numerals Hour numbers on a DIAL, once almost universally Roman, now usually Arabic. Today BATONS are often used instead.

Nuremberg Hours Early system of time reckoning in Nuremberg. The 24 hours in a day and night period were numbered afresh from 1 at each sunrise and sunset.

Nurnberg (Nuremberg) This town in the Bavarian district of Germany was one of the first centres of clockmaking, with Augsburg. In 1565 the Rat (mayor) issued a decree forming clockmakers, firearm makers, and locksmiths into a guild. Masterpieces had to be made by all men before they were allowed to practise their trade, those for clockmakers being an iron striking chiming and alarm clock six inches high in a brass case, or one of the big striking and alarm watches of the time worn on a ribbon round the neck.

Nurnberg Egg Some of the earliest watches were made in

NURNBERG in the early sixteenth century. Doppelmeyer, writing a history some 200 years later of the clockmakers there, called these watches 'eyerlein' or little eggs. He had mistranslated 'Ueurlein' meaning 'little clocks', but the false name still persists today, although these watches were ball shaped. A few egg-shaped watches were made in later years. *See* **Watch** *and* **Musk Ball Watch.**

Nutation A nodding movement of the Earth during its rotation, which affects its time of rotation (i.e. SIDEREAL TIME) to the extent of about 20 MILLISECONDS every 15 days, as well as by about 1.2 seconds over 18 years. Discovered in the eighteenth century but not applied in TIME DETERMINATION until 1926 when the SHORTT CLOCK could measure it. Sidereal time has to be corrected by a nutation figure to give mean sidereal time, in the same way as SOLAR TIME has to be corrected by the EQUATION OF TIME to give mean solar time.

Observatory Clock Clock for astronomical TIME DETERMINA-TIONS. The very first mechanical clocks with VERGE ESCAPEMENT and FOLIOT, may well have been those that drove GLOBES and other astronomical mechanisms, which only later were simplified for domestic use. The CROSS BEAT followed for astronomical use, but as more accurate time measurements were demanded, astronomers employed a weight on a cord and counted the swings. This was developed into the PENDULUM CLOCK which was made more accurate by the ANCHOR ESCAPEMENT and still more by the DEAD BEAT, in clocks called REGULATORS. The RIEFLER CLOCK bettered timekeeping and was itself much improved on by the SHORTT CLOCK, in turn replaced by the QUARTZ CLOCK, which the ATOMIC CLOCK is now superseding. Some observatory clocks show SIDEREAL TIME and have TWENTY-FOUR HOUR DIALS. *See* **Time Determination, Royal Greenwich Observatory, Greenwich Observatory** *and* **Octagon Room.**

123

Octagon Room   The original room from which observations were made in GREENWICH OBSERVATORY. It contained two fine clocks with 13 ft. PENDULUMS above them, specially made by Thos. TOMPION for John FLAMSTEED. These clocks now belong to the BRITISH MUSEUM and the Earl of Leicester, but replicas are in their place at Greenwich.

Oignon   French watches of the early eighteenth century which were larger and thicker than the English and therefore called 'onions'. After 1800, French watches became delicate and original and English ones stolidly reliable.

Oil   Problems of oiling have always been of great concern to watch and clock makers and still are today. The famous BREGUET said to Napoleon: 'Give me a perfect oil, and I will give you a perfect watch.' This is still true of mechanical watches, yet the public is entirely ignorant of the fact. To give their best service, clocks and watches should be cleaned and re-oiled every two years or so because, unlike other mechanisms, they never stop, day or night, and the extremely tiny amounts of various types of oil in them eventually must dry out, become gummy, or become a kind of grinding paste with dust. Modern horological oils and greases have considerable scientific research behind them. Some are natural and others are synthetic. Church records of 1498 refer to applying 'cowes fatt oil to the pivotts of the clocke'. Freezing of the oil used to stop church clocks, and various inventions of non-freezing oils included calves foot oil mixed with Scotch fir tar, and fish oil with pepper, and other oddities. The problem still arises during arctic and space exploration. Most early makers used animal fat oils—such as neat's foot, sheep's foot, and whale oil (a famous one came from the nose of the porpoise) and vegetable oils—such as olive and palm which they filtered and blended themselves. Mineral oils were not used until the end of the nineteenth century. They usually have to have some animal oil added to improve their wetting properties. Lord GRIMTHORPE advised neat's foot oil for TOWER CLOCKS. Some clockmakers, including HARRISON, tried to eliminate oils altogether. Another problem that still exists is to prevent oil spread. The tiny drops should be held in place by surface tension, like drops of water in the holes of a tea strainer. This is helped by OIL SINKS, but it is not possible to place them on all parts. After ULTRASONIC CLEANING a special coating known as 'EPILAME' is given to the movement to avoid oil spread. The oiling of a precision watch requires considerable skill and knowledge. Too much, or too little, or oil in the wrong places, can affect the RATE of clocks (including tower clocks) and stop smaller watches.

Oil Sink A small well around a PIVOT in a clock or watch PLATE or JEWEL which retains the oil. *See* **Sully** *and* **Le Roy**.

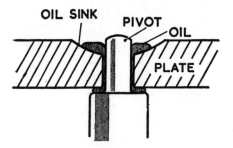

Fig. 21. Oil sink.

Oliver Cromwell's Watch A plain PURITAN WATCH on a FOB chain which belonged to the Protector and is now in the BRITISH MUSEUM COLLECTION. It was made in 1625 by John Midnall of Fleet Street.

One-Hand Clocks Before about 1400, clocks had one fixed hand and a dial that turned (*see* **Monastery Clock**). Then the dial became fixed and a single hour hand turned. Minute hands were introduced soon after on special clocks, but not generally until after mid-seventeenth century for domestic clocks. Cheaper clocks still continued for some years with one hand. The present Westminster Abbey clock still has only one hand. *See* **Hand, Clock** *and* **Hand, Watch.**

One-Wheel Clock   There was much competition at one time to produce clocks with the fewest gear wheels. A one-wheel clock is recorded in 1598. Pierre LE ROY made an astronomical one, and Lepaute one showing seconds in mid-eighteenth century.

Organ Clock   Clock playing a small pipe organ every three hours. Popular in the second half of the eighteenth century, particularly for export to the East.

Ormskirk Escapement   An ESCAPEMENT for watches employed by English makers in the Ormskirk area in the 1800 period. Invented by Debaufré in 1704. Also called the 'chaffcutter', because the double ESCAPE WHEEL looks like one, or the 'club-footed verge'.

Orrery   Mechanical model showing the motions of Earth and Moon round the Sun. Named after the Earl of Cork and Orrery. Sometimes worked by clockwork from which it could be disengaged for demonstration. A famous one was made by TOMPION and GRAHAM.

Out of Beat   A PENDULUM releases a tooth of the ESCAPE WHEEL at the end of each swing. If this action is not symmetrical the clock is 'out of beat' and TICKS are alternately loud and soft, or the clock stops because a tooth is not released. The clock itself can be levelled to set it 'in beat', or a more permanent adjustment made by bending the CRUTCH in the direction of the loud PALLET. Other escapements on clocks and watches can become out of beat. To adjust the LEVER ESCAPEMENT for BEAT

126

it is necessary to alter the POINT OF ATTACHMENT of the HAIR-SPRING. Some watches have special devices to allow the outer point of attachment to be moved without dismantling the balance assembly.

Ovalizing Balance   A BI-METALLIC BALANCE which is not a CUT BALANCE. The arm (spokes) does not expand in the same proportion as the rim as temperature rises, so the balance becomes oval, and, combined with a modern alloy HAIRSPRING, can be arranged to give excellent TEMPERATURE COMPENSATION. First invented by Volet, a Frenchman, in the eighteenth century and reinvented independently by Lord Charnwood in the U.K. in 1927, and the Hamilton Watch Co. in the U.S.A. in 1942 for their MARINE CHRONOMETERS and DECK WATCHES, theirs having a stainless steel rim and an arm of INVAR.

Overcoil   A HAIRSPRING with the outer quarter turn raised and curved towards the centre. An ordinary spiral spring does not keep good time because the spring becomes lopsided as it opens and closes while the BALANCE swings. The overcoil avoids this. *See* **Breguet Spring.**

Over Compensation   A plain BALANCE AND SPRING will *lose* time as the temperature rises because of TEMPERATURE ERROR. If it has TEMPERATURE COMPENSATION and *gains* in heat, it is said to be 'over compensated'.

Pair Case   Extra detachable case round early highly decorated watches for protection. Some had a plain silver or gold inner case into which the MOVEMENT was hinged, then a separate decorative case, then a third, protective, case. The ordinary pair case of the eighteenth century had a plain inner and single outer case to keep out the dust, but some were ENAMELLED or otherwise decorated (Plate 7).

127

Pallet   The part of an escapement that intercepts the teeth of the ESCAPE WHEEL. Jewelled pallets made of synthetic ruby are better for watches and clocks than PIN PALLETS made of steel. *See* Fig. 17 *and* **Lever Escapement.**

Parachute Index   Combined SHOCK ABSORBER and regulation INDEX for watch BALANCE WHEELS invented by BREGUET. Forerunner of the modern shock absorber.

Parliament's Clocks   Clocks for the House of Commons, which was restored after damage during the Second World War, were the gift of Northern Ireland. One hundred and seventy-two SLAVE DIALS, split into six groups, are operated from a MASTER CLOCK through a control panel in the switch room. For timing divisions of the House, the Speaker has a special INTERVAL TIMER. The tower clock is popularly called 'BIG BEN'.

Pavement Clock   Clock set flush in the pavement or sidewalk with a heavy glass dial. There is one near Windsor Castle.

Pedometer Watch   The first SELF-WINDING WATCH was a pocket watch with a weighted lever, like that in a pedometer, which jerked when the wearer moved and wound the MAIN-SPRING. Made also by BREGUET.

Pegwood   Stripped twig of boxwood sharpened at the end like a pencil and used to clean out the PIVOT HOLES of clocks and watches.

Pendant   The 'hanging' part of a pocket watch, i.e. the part to which the 'bow' or loop is fixed. Since KEYLESS WINDING, the 'pendant position' of any watch is where its WINDING BUTTON (also called the 'crown') is fitted. The expression is used when checking POSITIONAL ERRORS, i.e. 'pendant right'.

Pendulum A weight swinging under the influence of gravity. First it was hung from a thread and the swings counted for astronomical time measurements. GALILEO discovered that the swing or BEAT depended only on the length of the thread or pendulum rod, not the angle of swing or weight of the BOB. HUYGENS proved this was only true if the pendulum swung through a cycloidal curve instead of the arc of a circle, the difference being CIRCULAR ERROR. Of several applications of a pendulum to clock mechanisms, that by Huygens was most successful. The RATE of a pendulum is altered by the different forces of gravity in different parts of the world. The formula is: time of swing in seconds equals the square root of the length in inches divided by 32, which gives approximately 39 in. (a metre) for a SECONDS PENDULUM. This measurement is made from the point of SUSPENSION to the CENTRE OF OSCILLATION of the BOB. The pendulum controls the RATE of a clock MOVEMENT and is kept swinging by IMPULSES from the ESCAPEMENT. *See* **Rating Nut, Conical Pendulum** *and* **Torsion Pendulum.**

Pendulum Rod Rod holding the BOB, made of brass, steel, varnished wood such as fir (which is not so much affected by temperature). COMPENSATION PENDULUM rods are made from INVAR or composite materials.

Pendulum Watch After the application of the PENDULUM to clocks, watchmakers who did not truly appreciate its theory tried to apply it to watches. A pendulum replaced the BALANCE and the watch was set in gimbals so that it would always stay upright. The case was therefore ball-shaped. This did not work well, so a counterbalance was added to the pendulum and it really became a DUMBELL BALANCE again. Most so-called pendulum watches were made after about 1700 and are false, being designed as a 'sales stunt' of the time to take advantage of the reputation of the pendulum. A disc was attached to the balance and could be seen oscillating through a slot in the dial, like the MOCK PENDULUM of a clock.

Perpetual Calendar Calendar worked by a clock which corrects for months of different lengths (and sometimes for leap year also). Occasionally incorporated in COMPLICATED WATCHES.

Perpetual Watch Name for the SELF-WINDING WATCHES made by BREGUET.

Phillips Curve A special curve or OVERCOIL of the outer end of a HAIRSPRING towards the centre to improve ISOCHRONISM, worked out mathematically by Edouard Phillips, a Frenchman, in 1860. The curves were further improved by another mathematician, Lossier of Geneva, around 1907. *See* **Breguet Spring.**

Phonic Motor An elementary motor which can be kept in step with an alternating electric current, like a SYNCHRONOUS CLOCK. Its consumption of electricity is so low that it can be driven from a radio valve; it is therefore commonly used to drive the hands or DIGITAL counters of a QUARTZ CLOCK.

Photographic Timer A switching device connected to a photographic enlarger. The dial is set to the time of printing exposure. A switch is pressed which sets the timer going and switches on the enlarger light. The light is switched out automatically at the end of the time set. A simpler form is a TIMER or ELAPSED TIME INDICATOR that rings a bell.

Picture Frame Clock The round DIAL is set in velvet in a picture frame, with brass SPANDRELS. Made from about 1875 to 1900 in France with green, blue or red velvet.

Pierpont Morgan Collection Magnificent collection of watches now in the Metropolitan Museum, New York. A superb catalogue of this in a limited edition of 46 copies was produced.

130

One is in the ILBERT LIBRARY at THE BRITISH HOROLOGICAL INSTITUTE.

Pigeon Clock   Special TIME RECORDER for pigeon racing. Birds are taken to the starting place and released. On each bird's arrival at its particular 'home' an identification ring from its leg is placed in a pigeon clock there. This records the time on a paper chart in hours and minutes and seals rings in a storage magazine in order of insertion. There are several devices to prevent the clock from being 'fiddled'.

Pillar Clock   French DRUM CLOCK with round movement and dial on four vertical pillars standing on a round base. The pendulum hangs in the middle of the pillars. Made in marble, ormolu, and wood in the nineteenth century. Also a special form of JAPANESE CLOCK showing time by a pointer moving along a linear scale, or any clock on a pillar.

Pillars   The riveted or screwed rods which fasten the PLATES together to make a clock FRAME or early watch frame. Formerly they were carved or turned in fancy shapes.

Pinion   One of the small solid, and usually steel, gear wheels in a clock or watch. The large gears are called 'wheels'. Formerly 'pinion wire' with the cross section of a gear, could be bought for cutting into pinions. The teeth are called 'leaves'. *See* **Wheel** *and* **Lantern Pinion.**

Pin Lever   Alternative name for a PIN-PALLET watch.

Pin-Pallet   An ESCAPEMENT with steel pins instead of jewelled PALLETS, used in cheap, particularly ROSCOPF, watches. The action is very similar to the LEVER ESCAPEMENT, and it is sometimes called 'pin lever'. Also the BROCOT ESCAPEMENT for clocks, which was not designed for cheapness.

Pin Wheel Clock ESCAPEMENT popular in France. Also employed in TURRET CLOCKS on the Continent. The teeth of the ESCAPE WHEEL are replaced by pins. A swinging pair of levers attached to the PENDULUM allows the pins to 'escape' one by one, and this also IMPULSES the pendulum. It is accurate and needs only a small pendulum arc. Invented by Amant in 1741.

Pinchbeck, Christopher (1651–1713) Inventor and maker of musical clocks, which gained world-wide repute, and of the metal alloy still called 'Pinchbeck'. Worked in Fleet Street, 'at the sign of the Astronomico—Musical Clock'. The 'curious secret of new-invented metal which so naturally resembles gold' was four parts copper to three zinc. His eldest son, also Christopher, made an ASTRONOMICAL CLOCK for King George III, which is still in the ROYAL COLLECTION.

Pinwork Watch PAIR CASE of leather, studded with silver pins (Plate 7).

Piqué Tortoiseshell inlaid with a decoration of silver or gold, used for watch PAIR CASES in the eighteenth century.

Pith Used by watchmakers for cleaning delicate watch parts.

Pivot The small end of a shaft or ARBOR that runs in a bearing hole. As special shape is necessary for BALANCE STAFF pivots that run in jewels, CONE PIVOTS are employed for cheap watches, alarm clocks, and many meters.

Pivoted Detent A form of DETENT ESCAPEMENT (as used on early MARINE CHRONOMETERS). The lever or detent which releases the ESCAPE WHEEL turns on a PIVOT. Now replaced by the SPRING DETENT.

Planetarium Representation of the night sky on a dome by complicated sets of projection lenses driven by clockwork. The only British one is at Madame Tussauds, in London, but another is to be built at GREENWICH OBSERVATORY.

Plate A front and a back plate of brass are joined by turned PILLARS to make a clock FRAME. In early watches top and bottom plates were similarly employed. Early clocks had elaborate engraved decoration, such as TULIP, over the backplate. Plates of MARINE CHRONOMETERS are usually SPOTTED. Those of some watches and small clocks are matted and GILDED, and of some machine-made clocks PRINKED.

Plate Clock *See* Telleruhr.

Platform Escapement An ESCAPEMENT (usually LEVER) on a small separate platform, usually across the PLATES of a clock. Usually driven by a CONTRATE WHEEL.

Plato Clock American name for a TICKET CLOCK.

Pocket Chronometer A high grade pocket watch with a DETENT ESCAPEMENT and CYLINDRICAL HAIRSPRING, made particularly over the end of the eighteenth and throughout the nineteenth century (even after the LEVER ESCAPEMENT became general). PIVOTED DETENTS were incorporated before about 1780 and SPRING DETENTS afterwards. The pocket chronometer is liable to POSITIONAL ERRORS and particularly affected by shock, reasons why it was surpassed by the LEVER. The seconds hand has DEAD BEAT action. Principal makers included the ARNOLDS, EARNSHAW, Dent, BREGUET, COLE, Jump, and Frodsham. The Swiss definition is a pocket watch, with lever or other escapement, that has gained a RATING CERTIFICATE.

Pocket Watch Watch introduced after the invention of the pocket in the first quarter of the seventeenth century and very popular after 1675, when the waistcoat became fashionable.

133

Now largely superseded by the WRIST-WATCH, except for men's dress wear and precision timekeeping, as a pocket watch is more accurate because of its larger size and reduced liability to POSITIONAL ERRORS, being kept in a vertical position most of the time. A TOURBILLON or a KARRUSEL practically eliminates errors in vertical positions. *See* **Pair Case.**

Point of Attachment   Usually the point at which the inner end of the HAIRSPRING is fixed to the BALANCE. Also called the 'pinning point'. It is impossible to fix this end on the exact axis of the BALANCE STAFF. As the end is therefore slightly out of centre, this causes movement of the centre of gravity of the HAIRSPRING and therefore small changes in RATE. Manipulation of this end of the balance is one of the fine ADJUSTMENTS carried out by watch ADJUSTERS.

Poise   Watchmaker's name for being in 'balance', or more exactly in 'static balance'. A BALANCE WHEEL is poised by adjusting the weight around the rim, either by removing metal, screwing screws around the rim in or out, or altering washers under the screws. An 'out-of-poise' balance causes increased POSITIONAL ERRORS.

Portable Sundial   Since a normal sundial had to be fixed in a certain and permanent position, portable sundials were valuable to military leaders and others before the portable clock was invented. There are two types, COMPASS DIAL and ALTITUDE DIAL. One of the earliest known is a silver and gold Saxon pocket sundial of label shape on a chain of the tenth century found in 1939 in the soil of the Cloister Garth of Canterbury Cathedral. It is an altitude dial showing TIDES.

Positional Errors   A watch runs at different RATES in different positions owing to ESCAPEMENT ERROR, lack of ISOCHRONISM, changes in the centre of gravity of the BALANCE and HAIRSPRING owing to the fact that the inner end of the spring cannot be fixed in the exact centre, and so on. The rate in wear is an average of these errors and therefore varies with different wearers. A good wrist-watch is tested and regulated in six positions, dial up, dial down, button up, button down, button right, button left. Worst errors are kept to the button left position, which occurs rarely with the watch on the outside of the left wrist. (A precision watch on the inside of the left wrist will give its worst performance.) A good watch which is a few seconds fast can be brought to time by leaving it on edge overnight, as it loses slightly in this position. Cheap wrist-watches are checked and regulated in two positions. Positional errors do not have so much effect on POCKET WATCHES and none at all on clocks.

Postman's Alarm   Alarm wall clock, with long PENDULUM and weights hanging below it, two brass bells on top, and outside hands. Made in Germany, modified in England, and popular up to 1939.

Potence   Form of COCK used as a lower bearing.

Prague Town Hall Clock   One of Europe's finest astronomical clocks built in 1490, renovated in 1866, destroyed in the Second World War and reconstructed after it.

Precession of the Equinox   Effect caused by the Earth turning like a dying top so that the axis has a slow conical motion. This causes a day of SIDEREAL TIME to be 9 MILLISECONDS shorter than the true period of rotation of the Earth. Discovered in 130 B.C. by Hipparchus. NUTATION is another disturbance in rotation. In addition, it was discovered in 1953 by QUARTZ CRYSTAL CLOCKS and confirmed by the ATOMIC CLOCK, that the Earth is slowing down.

135

Precision Clock Any clock made for very accurate time-keeping, such as a REGULATOR, FREE PENDULUM CLOCK, electric MASTER CLOCK, QUARTZ CLOCK or CHRONOMETER clock with CONSTANT FORCE ESCAPEMENT or DEAD BEAT ESCAPEMENT, OBSERVATORY CLOCK, etc.

Precision Watch Quality watch which has been individually adjusted and holds a RATING CERTIFICATE. *See* **Chronometer.**

Prescot, Lancashire. Once a centre of the BRITISH HOROLOGICAL INDUSTRY, especially about 1850, making most parts of watches (and the best files in Europe) by hand methods for assemblers in COVENTRY, CLERKENWELL, etc. Two watchmaker-inventors, John Wycherley and T. P. Hewitt, caused a revival later, then the Lancashire Watch Co. (1888) and Prescot Watch Factory were opened, but hand craftsmen resisted the trend and the trade went to Switzerland.

Prime Meridian The zero MERIDIAN LINE which passes through GREENWICH OBSERVATORY and on which the world's time measurements and TIME ZONES are based. The Observatory is now in Sussex and not on the meridian, so corrections have to be made for this in TIME DETERMINATION.

Prinked A prinked clock PLATE has small dots impressed in rows on it to harden the surface.

Process Timer Clock for timing a manufacturing process. Sometimes a separate large TIMER, at others an ELAPSED TIME INDICATOR, or TIME SWITCH, which actually controls the process.

Production Timer A TIMER used to measure the time of making a single article. The hand then indicates the rate of production per hour.

Programme Controller Large cam which turns under the control of a MASTER CLOCK and rings bells, such as for school lessons changes, or operates switches to carry out some other programme. Programme times can be completely changed or varied on different days of the week.

Pull Repeater A REPEATER CLOCK with a cord from each side which is pulled to make it sound the time. Useful for nights before matches were invented (Plate 1).

Pulse Meter TIMER calibrated to give pulse rate per min. by timing 30 beats.

Pump Winding Early form of KEYLESS WINDING by 'pumping' a knob on the watch which wound the MAINSPRING through a ratchet mechanism.

Puritan Watch Oval shaped pocket watch with rounded edges and plain case only about 2 in. long, commonly made in England in the seventeenth century (Plate 5).

Push Button Regulator Modern watch with a small push button in the case to alter the regulation without opening the case. One version has a button which puts the watch to time on the TIME SIGNAL and REGULATES it automatically at the same time. *See* **Sympathetic Clock.**

Push Piece A press button on a watch case for operating additional mechanisms such as a CHRONOGRAPH, AUTOMATON, SPLIT SECONDS HAND, etc.

Quail Clock Similar to a CUCKOO CLOCK but its bellows imitate the quail.

Quality Standards The quality of a timepiece depends on design, sound construction, finish, timekeeping abilities, etc. Most tests are for timekeeping only (*see* **Rating Certificate**) but

137

quality standard tests are applied to some manufacture, the best known being the French Cétéhor standard. There are certain British Standards, but they are not compulsory.

Quare, Daniel (1649–1724)   A Quaker who refused to take the oath of allegiance to become clockmaker to George I, but nevertheless was granted the office and permission to use the back stairs! Invented a REPEATER watch (now in the ASHMOLEAN MUSEUM) about six years before BARLOW and successfully opposed his application for a patent. Also made fine barometers, and thin watches only $\frac{1}{5}$ in. between PLATES.

Quarter Boy   The JACK that strikes the quarter hours on a clock with AUTOMATA.

Quarter Repeater   Clock or watch REPEATER that repeats hours and quarters, but not minutes. Thus four strokes followed by three TING TANG notes indicates three quarters after four, i.e. 4.45.

Quartz Crystal Clock (Quartz clock)   Electronic clock accurate to the equivalent of about 1 sec. in 30 years; invented by W. A. Marrison in the U.S.A., in 1929. A slice of quartz or ESSEN RING given alternate charges of electricity at the appropriate frequency resonates like a piano string. This is known as the piezo-electric effect. Such a crystal cut to vibrate at 100,000 cycles a second controls an oscillating circuit with extreme accuracy, acting like the ESCAPEMENT of a mechanical clock. The frequency is broken down by frequency dividers to 100 cycles per second and this operates a PHONIC MOTOR to show time or operate TIME SIGNALS. Observatories use large crystal clocks (OBSERVA-TORY CLOCKS) in groups of six or so. All have their own temperature-controlled crystals kept in a special chamber like a prison cell. The rates are compared with SIDEREAL (or star) TIME. Royal Observatory quartz clocks are better timekeepers than the Earth. Small quartz clocks (ELECTRONIC CHRONO-METERS) are used for measuring short time intervals in industry and in RATE RECORDERS for checking watch RATES.

Queen Charlotte's Watch The most influential watch ever made, as it incorporated the first LEVER ESCAPEMENT which eventually revolutionized watch and clock accuracy and manufacture. Made by Thos. MUDGE in 1759. He thought little of it and, as it was so difficult to make, no other appeared until 1782, when Josiah Emery improved it by introducing DRAW. After about 1825, it gradually became universal. The original watch, made to the order of King George III, is in the ROYAL COLLECTION and is kept at Windsor Castle. (The King was very interested in horology, had lessons in repairing, and had his own observatory in Richmond Park.) It is in a gold PAIR CASE about 2½ in. in diameter and 1¼ in. thick, with enamelled dial, and CENTRE SECONDS HAND. There is a SOLID BALANCE wheel with TEMPERATURE COMPENSATION by BI-METALLIC COMPENSATION CURB.

Rack Clock A GRAVITY CLOCK in which the whole clock slowly slides down a toothed rack on a stand. A PINION in the clock is driven by engaging the rack.

Rack Lever A transitional LEVER ESCAPEMENT before MUDGE's detached lever. Invented by the Abbé d'Hautefeuille in 1722. Many were made in England by Peter Litherland, Roskell, and others, of Liverpool, after 1791.

Rack Striking Method of 'counting', i.e. controlling strikes of a clock, invented by BARLOW in 1676 and now universal. At the hour, a toothed arm (the rack) drops on to a cam and is wound back a number of teeth equal to the strokes. The cam, which is snail shaped, turns with the hour hand, therefore striking cannot get out of sequence as with the LOCKING PLATE used formerly. It may be damaged by turning hands backwards in older clocks; in modern ones there is provision for avoiding damage.

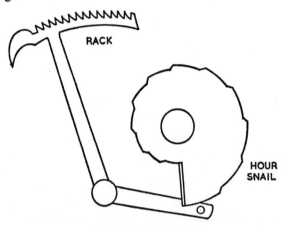

Fig. 22. Rack striking.

Radio Time Signal The first were from the Eiffel Tower, Paris, and Nordeich, Germany, in 1914. The Greenwich time signal began in 1923 along a wire from GREENWICH OBSERVATORY to the B.B.C. Savoy Hill Studio, but is now from the time department of the Observatory at Abinger Common, Surrey, to B.B.C. headquarters (*see* **Six Pips**). Signals are corrected for land line delay. 'BIG BEN'S' first stroke at the hour was also used from 31 December 1923. Continuous time signals or frequency standards monitored by the ATOMIC CLOCK are broadcast from the Post Office radio station at Rugby (MSF), the U.S. Bureau of Standards (WWV), and transmitters in Switzerland (HBN), Italy (IBF), and Czechoslovakia (OMA). *See* **Time Signal.**

Railway Time When railways spread over the country in the nineteenth century, they had to keep their own MEAN TIME

140

because places through which they passed used LOCAL TIMES. They issued leaflets giving conversion figures from local times to Railway Time. Eventually both became GREENWICH MEAN TIME.

Raingo, M. French maker of fine ORRERY clocks in the nineteenth century. Five are in England—at Windsor in the ROYAL COLLECTION; in Soane's Museum, London; the Glasgow Art Gallery; and private collections—one is in the Paul Chamberlain Collection, U.S.A., and others in Paris, Madrid and Brussels.

Ramsay, David (d. about 1654) Chief clockmaker to King James I. Probably came from Dalhousie, Scotland. In the VICTORIA AND ALBERT MUSEUM are a watch and clock by him. He appears with a shop near Temple Bar in Sir Walter Scott's novel *The Fortunes of Nigel*.

Rate The regularity of going of a clock or watch, regardless of how much is gaining or losing. A watch that gains, say, exactly three seconds every day has a perfect rate. One that gains a few seconds one day and loses some the next has a bad rate although it frequently shows the correct time of day.

Rate Recorder Machine also called a 'timing machine', for printing the instantaneous RATE of a watch or clock. It comprises a QUARTZ CLOCK which controls the feed of a paper tape. The ticks of the TIMEPIECE are amplified and printed on the tape to produce a dotted line. The slope of the line gives the exact rate of the timepiece in a few seconds. Used for bringing to MEAN TIME and for checking POSITIONAL ERRORS: also for fault finding, since OUT OF BEAT, MAGNETIZED, and other conditions are shown at once. Without a machine, each daily check takes 24 hours.

Rating Certificate There are two main classes of testing. Tests for special timekeepers are carried out at the NATIONAL PHYSICAL LABORATORY, England; Geneva Observatory, Switzerland; and German Hydrographic Institute, and special certificates issued. Swiss production watches of high performance are sold with rating certificates issued by one of the Official Bureaux for testing watches. Only those gaining certificates can by law be called 'CHRONOMETERS'. These tests are for 15 days in five positions and different temperatures. The French have a scheme covering QUALITY STANDARDS as well as timing tests and watches are marked with stars according to results. The Swiss, Japanese and Russian industries also have general quality standards.

Rating Nut   Nut below a pendulum BOB for screwing it up or down to alter the clock's rate. On SECONDS PENDULUMS, a $\frac{5}{16}$ in. Whitworth thread makes one minute a day difference for one turn of the nut.

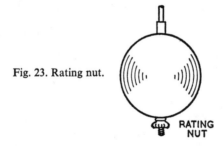

Fig. 23. Rating nut.

RATING NUT

Raw Movement   Another name for an EBAUCHE.

Recoil Escapement   Another name for the ANCHOR ESCAPEMENT because the wheels turn back a little after every jump forward. This 'recoil' can be seen by watching the seconds hand of a LONG CASE CLOCK.

Recoiling Click   A form of STOP WORK applied particularly to watches to prevent their being overwound. In the simplest version, the click (ratchet pawl) which holds up the MAINSPRING has a slot instead of a hole for its bearing. Thus when a watch is wound up as far as it will go, the click will recoil and let down the spring a little as soon as the winding button is released (Fig. 26). There are many other versions.

'Record' Tompion   Magnificent LONG CASE CLOCK made about 1699 for King William III by Thos. TOMPION, probably for Hampton Court Palace. It has a fine case with gilded mounts and a figure of Minerva on the top. The plinth base is of cast and chased metal, the only other Tompion clock with this being in Buckingham Palace. The clock runs for three months at a winding and has a PERPETUAL CALENDAR. Given by Queen Victoria to the Duke of Cambridge, it was sold at Christies in 1904 for 125 guineas, reappeared in the Dunn Collection and sold in 1911 for 380 guineas, appeared in the WETHERFIELD COLLECTION and sold in 1928 across the Atlantic; then bought back by an English collector, J. S. Sykes, for £4,000. In 1956 it was sold again to the U.S.A., when Williamsburg, Virginia, bought it for £11,000, despite attempts to stop the sale, because of the clock's historic value. The origin of the name 'Record' is not known.

Registered Horological Retailer   Watch and clock retailers who are members of the BRITISH HOROLOGICAL INSTITUTE and agree to abide by certain high standard of trading are issued with special plaques which customers should look out for as it gives them protection against unfair salesmanship.

Registered Watchmaker   The BRITISH HOROLOGICAL INSTITUTE keeps an illuminated record of craftsmen who have qualified by examination and have had so many years' experience. They are allowed to show a special plaque. To protect themselves, the public should always go to one of these watch repairers. In the U.S.A. and Canada, watchmakers are registered in some states which insist upon certain minimum qualifications.

Regulation Adjusting the RATE of a timepiece. Precision of regulation depends on the design, quality, and condition of the timepiece. Accurate regulation of a clock is much easier than of a watch because it is normally stationary. Every watch goes at different rates in different positions and has to be regulated to average the errors. Also it will go about 10 sec. a day slower in wear and has to be adjusted to suit the wearer if a high-grade watch. To speed adjustment, watchmakers use RATE RECORDERS. In the factory or after major repair the BALANCE is POISED, and HAIRSPRING timed, and the assembly 'timed' by rate recorder before being mounted in the watch; then the outer end of the hairspring is 'pinned up' and the assembly SET IN BEAT. Next, adjustments are made to reduce POSITIONAL ERRORS as much as possible. In wrist-watches the worst errors are left in the unimportant 'winding button right' position (as when the watch is worn on the inside of the left wrist). The watch should now have a good rate so that final regulation to bring it to MEAN TIME can be done by moving the INDEX. High-grade watches are sometimes FREE SPRUNG which means they have no index, being regulated by TIMING SCREWS or nuts on the balance wheel. A clock with balance and spring is regulated similarly except that positional errors are not now important. A PENDULUM clock is regulated by moving the BOB up or down by a RATING NUT. Precision pendulum clocks have a tray part way down the pendulum rod on which small weights can be placed to raise the effective height of the bob and make the clock gain, a halfpenny on the tray of 'BIG BEN' for 24 hr., making it gain $\frac{1}{5}$ sec. Very early clocks were regulated by moving the weights on the FOLIOT in or out, and, if they had balance wheels without springs, by BRISTLE REGULATOR and by SETTING UP the MAIN-SPRING or altering the driving weight. Early watch balances with hairsprings had a REGULATOR (turned by a key which moved a toothed wheel) to adjust the hairspring length. *See* **Temperature Error, Barometric Error, Circular Error, Isochronism, Tourbillon.**

Regulator Very accurate LONG CASE CLOCK usually with DEAD BEAT, PIN WHEEL or GRAVITY ESCAPEMENT, TEMPERATURE COMPENSATED pendulum and no striking or other complication. The dial usually has three separate CHAPTER RINGS for the long central minute hand, the shorter hour hand below it, and seconds hand above it. The case is usually plain.

Regulator, Clock *See* **Rise and Fall Regulator** *and* **Regulation.**

Regulator, Watch Device for regulating the timekeeping of a watch. Before the HAIRSPRING was invented this was done by SETTING-UP the MAINSPRING by a ratchet and dial provided, and by BRISTLE REGULATOR. The first to adjust the effective length of the hairspring was TOMPION in the 1660s. A dial on the back of the MOVEMENT was turned by a key. The dial was geared to a segment carrying CURB PINS between which ran the end of the hairspring. This idea persisted until nearly 1800. About the same time, BARROW employed a threaded rod which moved a nut carrying curb pins, but it did not become popular. On the Continent Tompion's scheme was favoured except for the use of a moving pointer and fixed dial. The next development was a movable ring, carrying curb pins and a pointer, fitted round the hairspring. This developed into the INDEX on the BALANCE COCK, a pointer fitted friction tight round the JEWEL or SHOCK ABSORBER, which carried the curb pins. It is used on modern watches, and has been developed into the auxiliary regulator or index, which has an additional friction ring carrying the index pins, so that after the watch is adjusted by the factory the index pointer can be set to a central position.

Remembrance Watch A watch in which the numerals 1 to 12 are replaced by the letters of a person's name, or a message.

145

Remontoire Device which applies a controlled force to IMPULSE the PENDULUM or BALANCE to overcome variations in timekeeping caused particularly by variations in the driving motor. One way is to wind up a small weight (invented by HUYGENS in 1659). Another keeps 'reloading' a small spring. John HARRISON used this in 1739. The modern Secticon battery clock has a spring remontoire. The GRAVITY ESCAPEMENT and the GRAVITY ARM of an ELECTRONIC MASTER CLOCK are both forms of remontoire. Also called a 'constant force escapement'.

Repeater Alarm A modern alarm clock that rings in short bursts with an interval of about half a minute between them. A SYNCHRONOUS version allows the sleeper ten minutes' 'dozing time'.

Repeater Clock Before the days of artificial light, it was difficult to read a clock at night without the performance of lighting a candle with flint and tinder. Some of the best BRACKET CLOCKS could therefore be made to repeat the time on bells. Usually there is a cord with a button on the end from each side of the clock which is pulled to load and operate the REPEATING WORK. This is called a 'pull repeater'. Most clocks are QUARTER REPEATERS, invented by Edward BARLOW in 1676; some are HALF-QUARTER REPEATERS, and a few FIVE MINUTE REPEATERS. MINUTE REPEATERS are known from the eighteenth century. The repeater clock went out of fashion when matches were invented in the first quarter of the nineteenth century.

Repeater Watch A pocket watch which will repeat the time on a bell, GONG, or the watch case itself. Intended mainly for use in the dark. The first, QUARTER REPEATERS, were invented by Edward BARLOW and Daniel QUARE near the end of the seventeenth century. BREGUET employed wire gongs in 1789. Other types are MINUTE (introduced in the nineteenth century), HALF QUARTER, and FIVE MINUTE REPEATER. There is no special winding button for the repeating work; on earlier watches the PENDANT of the watch is pressed and on later ones a slide on the side of the case is moved (which loads a spring) and when released sets the REPEATER going. *See* **Dumb Repeater.**

Repeating Work A form of COMPLICATED WORK enabling a REPEATER CLOCK or WATCH to strike the time at will. In watches this is complex and involves separate RACKS for repeating the hours, quarters, half quarters, five minutes, and minutes. *See* **Barlow.**

Repoussé Embossed designs, usually on silver or gold, most popular for watch cases in mid-eighteenth century.

Republican Time Attempted decimal division of the hour into 100 minutes by the French Revolutionaries. *See* **Decimal Clock.**

Revolving Band Clock Clocks in which a band marked with 12 or 24 hours revolves to indicate the time against a fixed pointer. Popular in France in the eighteenth century and used on clock cases shaped like urns, vases, and globes.

Riefler Clock Precision PENDULUM clock with TEMPERATURE COMPENSATION, invented by Riefler of Munich in 1889 and adopted as an OBSERVATORY CLOCK. The PENDULUM is almost FREE. It is IMPULSED by an arrangement that flexes the SUSPEN-SION SPRING of the pendulum first one way then the other. *See* **Accuracy of Clocks** *and* **Mercurial Pendulum.**

Ring Watch A watch mounted in a finger ring. Guido Ubaldo della Rovere, Duke of Urbino, is recorded as having had a CLOCK WATCH so mounted in 1542! John ARNOLD made a very small ring watch with 120 parts in 1764 for King George III. The MOVEMENT was only $\frac{1}{2}$ in. across. It had a CYLINDER ESCAPEMENT with a ruby cylinder, the first known, only $\frac{1}{54}$ in.

in diameter, and was a HALF-QUARTER REPEATER. It probably still exists although its present whereabouts are not known. Modern ring watches are made in quantity. *See* **Smallest Watch** (Plates 1 *and* 8).

Rise and Fall Regulator Early arrangement for adjusting the length of a PENDULUM from the top, by moving the SUSPENSION SPRING in a slot. Alternative to screwing the bob of a PENDULUM up or down for timekeeping REGULATION.

Rock Crystal Transparent quartz used for decoration, 'glasses', CASES, and even PLATES, of clocks and watches from the earliest days.

Rolled Gold Thin layer of gold which has been soldered to a base metal such as nickel and rolled out thinner. A British Standard of 1960 requires rolled gold watch cases to be marked 'R' followed by the thickness of gold in microns (thousandths of a millimetre) thus: R 20 M. Cases used to be stamped with the number 5, 10, 15 or 20 according to how many years the rolled gold was expected to last.

Rolling Ball Clock *See* **Ball Clock** (Plate 6).

Rolling Clock Form of GRAVITY CLOCK (without mainspring). The earliest still existing was made about 1600 by Isaac HABRECHT. The clock is drum-shaped and rolls slowly down an inclined board. The hand remains still and hour numerals turn with the case. Still made by Gübelin in Switzerland and Garrard in England, but the dial remains stationary and the hands turn normally. When the clock reaches the bottom of the inclined plane it is replaced at the top by hand (Plate 6). The inclined track is often marked with days of the week.

Roman Numerals These still persist on clock dials because of

148

their symmetry, which is why IIII is usually used (to balance the VIII) instead of IV. 'Big Ben' has IV.

Roman Striking Method of striking by Roman numerals instead of Arabic, invented by Joseph KNIBB to reduce winding. A high-pitched bell represents 1, a low pitched one V, and two blows on the low pitched one, X. Thus IX is sounded by a high-pitched note followed by two low ones.

Roscopf First cheap watch, a pocket watch made in 1865–67 by G. F. Roscopf, a German who settled in Switzerland. He eliminated the CENTRE WHEEL, which allowed him to use a big BARREL overlapping the centre of the watch. The ESCAPEMENT was a separate PIN-PALLET unit; the winding button could be turned only one way; there was no STOP WORK; the MOTION WORK turned on the barrel ARBOR; and the hands were set by turning them with one's finger. The 'people's watch' was steadily improved until today many millions of cheap wrist-watches are made on a modified Roscopf lay-out, in all watchmaking countries except, strangely, U.S.S.R., which makes only JEWELLED LEVERS.

Roskilde Cathedral Clock Early Danish 24-hour clock in Roskilde, with two jacks and St George slaying the dragon, which utters agonized cries!

Rotor Eccentric weight which winds the MAINSPRING of a SELF-WINDING WATCH, and can turn through a full circle, as opposed to the PEDOMETER WATCH weight, which has a limited swing. Many rotors wind the watch while turning either way.

Royal Clockmaker In earlier days of clockmaking in any country, appointment to the Court meant good business, and many famous makers held such positions. Nicholas CRATZER, clockmaker to Henry VIII in 1538, was the earliest known in

England. One of the most versatile was Peter Auguste Caron, who made watches for the French King, invented a VIRGULE ESCAPEMENT in 1753, and was a musician and author, writing *The. Marriage of Figaro* and *The Barber of Seville* under the name of 'Beaumarchais'. The appointment is still made in Britain, but to a retailer. There were sometimes separate appointments of Royal Watchmaker, but earlier makers produced both watches and clocks.

Royal Collection   This contains many magnificent clocks, most of which are in use in Windsor Castle, Buckingham Palace, St James's Palace, and Hampton Court. They include the ANNE BOLEYN CLOCK; an early Augsburg MUSICAL CLOCK by Jacob Mayr; ASTRONOMICAL CLOCKS by Julien LE ROY, RAINGO, PINCHBECK, Lepine, and Eardley Norton, whose version has four dials, one on each side. There are many fine French clocks, some with fine BUHL cases, including a SYMPATHETIC CLOCK, REGULATOR, and a two-pendulum (one for metronome use) clock by BREGUET and a YEAR CLOCK by Lepaute. Other clocks are by TOMPION (one has a 24-hr. dial and shows both EQUAL TIME and APPARENT TIME); QUARE (year clock); Isaac Duhamel; John Barwise; Richard Vick; Alex Cumming (month clock); and VULLIAMY. There are SKELETON CLOCKS designed by CONGREVE, a Negress head clock with hours and minutes in the eyes by Lepine and even a TAVERN CLOCK (at Windsor Castle).

Royal Greenwich Observatory   The English national observatory which was set up by the Admiralty in 1676, with John FLAMSTEED as its first ASTRONOMER ROYAL. His duty was to make star observations to assist navigation of ships, the problem of FINDING THE LONGITUDE, which was eventually solved by the MARINE CHRONOMETER. The Observatory eventually became responsible for TIME DETERMINATION and TIME DISTRIBUTION, and the maintenance of the Admiralty's MARINE CHRONOMETERS, etc., while continuing its astronomical work. In 1946 a move was made to Herstmonceux Castle in Sussex because the industrial haze over GREENWICH OBSERVATORY interfered with observations, but the name was not changed. *See also* **Airy, Observatory Clock, Octagon Room, Prime Meridian** *and* **Time Ball.**

Royal Pendulum Contemporary eighteenth-century name for the SECONDS PENDULUM.

Ruby Pin The pin made of synthetic ruby through which the lever of a LEVER ESCAPEMENT (Fig. 17) gives IMPULSE to the BALANCE. Also called 'impulse pin'. In PIN-PALLET escapements it is often of steel.

Russian Horological Industry In 1929 the Soviet Government started an industry by buying two complete American watch factories, the Duber Watch Co. and the Ansonia Watch Co., to set up the First and Second Moscow Watchmaking Plants respectively, which were extended and reconstructed in 1934–35, when two extra plants were set up in Kuibyshev and Prenza. During the Great Patriotic War (Second World War) watch-making plants were set up in the East at Christopol, Chelyabinsk, Zlatoust, and Serdobsk, then mainly for fuse making, and after the war others at Oryol, Yerevan, Minsk, Rostov-on-Don, Petrodvorets, Uglich, and elsewhere. Only JEWELLED LEVER watches are made in Russia. Clocks include all types. The industry has the world's biggest output after Switzerland. Technical control of the whole industry is under a single organization in Moscow. Yearly watch output is about 17% of world output but rising rapidly.

Rye Church Clock Oldest English clock still working in its original place, in Sussex. Made in 1515 and later converted to 2¼ sec. approx. pendulum, which hangs down inside the church.

St Mark's Clock Magnificent astronomical clock with AUTOMATA in St Mark's Square, Venice. It has tablet numerals.

St Paul's Cathedral Clock May have been England's first public clock. Records show that in 1286 the clock keeper 'Bartholomo Orologiario' was entitled to a loaf of bread daily. This clock was probably inside the nave. It was replaced in 1344. Such clocks had no dials or hands, but JACKS which struck bells. They were lighted with candles for services. The present clock was installed in 1893 and strikes on GREAT TOM, having been designed as a rival to 'BIG BEN'.

Salisbury Cathedral Clock The oldest clock (1386) still working. It was originally in a thirteenth century bell tower in the Close, and re-installed in the cathedral in the eighteenth century when the bell tower was demolished. Replaced by a new clock in 1884, it was 'lost' until discovered by T. R. Robinson in the tower in 1928, and cleaned and put on show in 1931. Many years ago it had been converted to pendulum. In 1956 it was restored to FOLIOT, with 4-sec. ticks, and set going again inside the cathedral. There is no dial. The frame and wheels are of wrought iron, the frame being held together with mortice and tenon joints with wedges like early furniture (Plate 3).

Salomons' Collection Famous collection, mainly of BREGUET's work, by the late Sir David Salomons.

Salt Cellar Clock 'The Salt'—the container holding salt—was often large and of gold or silver in the seventeenth century and an important item in state banquets—unimportant people being put 'below the salt'. A clock was occasionally incorporated in it.

Sand-Glass Early interval TIMER, comprising a glass globe, with a narrow waist, partly filled with sand (often powdered egg shell). When up-ended, the sand passes from the top to the bottom globe in a fixed time. If the time is an hour, the device is an hour-glass. Developed after WATER CLOCKS, having the advantage of not freezing. The earliest have two open glass bulbs with a pierced brass diaphragm between them. Sand was placed in one and the parts sealed by wax and bound with thread round the joint. The next type was introduced in the late seventeenth century and has two bulbs blown and drawn in one piece, one left with a hole at the top for insertion of the sand. The hole is stopped by a cloth-covered cork. Many have a copper diaphragm pressed into the waist. A third type, from early nineteenth century, is similar but the hole has been sealed by the glass blower. Some were constructed in batteries of three or more with different time intervals. Large ones were commonly stood on pulpits in the past to time sermons and called 'sermon glasses'. Used too, on ships, as late as 1839 even in the British Navy, to calculate speeds. For this a float or 'chip' at the end of a long line with knots at intervals was thrown over the side. The number of knots that ran out as timed by the sand-glass gave the speed in knots. The House of Commons has a 2-min. glass formerly employed for timing division bells calling Members to vote.

Satellite Timer Time switch for switching on and off the radio transmitter and receiver and other instruments in artificial satellites. If a radio operated by a solar battery were not switched off it might transmit indefinitely, unnecessarily blocking useful channels. In American satellites the basis of the timer is the ELECTRONIC WATCH.

Science Museum Collection The most interesting of all collection of timekeepers for the mechanically minded, covering not only a comprehensive historical range of instruments and inventions, but the history up to recent developments in electric clocks, MASTER CLOCKS, TIME SWITCHES, and GAS CONTROLLERS,

TIME RECORDERS, STOP-WATCHES, QUARTZ CRYSTAL and ATOMIC CLOCKS, etc., not shown by other collections. At South Kensington, London, S.W.7.

Scratch Dial Primitive SUNDIAL scratched on church walls from the twelfth to fifteenth century. *See* **Mass Dial.**

Screw Metal screws came into use on clocks about 1500 on the Continent, but not until nearly a century later in England. Previously, slots and wedges (as in early wooden furniture) were employed to make temporary joints, and permanent joints were usually fire welded.

Second The International Committee of Weights and Measures defines the second as one 31,556,925.9747th part of the year 1900. This is based on EPHEMERIS TIME. A second measured by the ATOMIC CLOCK is now known to be more accurate and may in future be adopted. It equals 9,192,631,770 vibrations of the caesium atom. The word was originally a 'second minute', i.e. the second division into 60.

Seconds Hand Hand of a clock or watch showing seconds. One of the earliest is on BURGI's rock crystal clock made just after 1600, but they did not come into general use on clocks until the LONG PENDULUM was invented and on watches until the CYLINDER ESCAPEMENT. *See* **Centre Seconds.**

Seconds Pendulum A PENDULUM taking a second to swing from one side to the other and therefore theoretically 39.14 in. long.

Secret Signature Because BREGUET's watches were faked, he put a secret signature on many as an indication of authenticity. This is a very tiny signature under the 12 on enamel dials and on either side of 12 on metal ones, on which it can be spotted by looking across the dial towards the light.

Sedan Clock   Small clock with a VERGE watch movement and often a circular wooden case about 6 in. across, for hanging in a sedan chair. Made in the late seventeenth and early eighteenth centuries.

Self-Correcting Chimes   Automatic arrangement on most domestic chiming clocks by which the chimes, if out of sequence, are held up at the hour and released when again in step.

Self-Winding Clock   Perhaps the first was driven by a fan in the kitchen chimney, as recorded by Gaspar Schott in 1664. Very many types have been invented. *See* **Light Clock, Atmospheric Clock, Automatic Winding** *and* **Battery Clock.**

Self-Winding Watch   Watch wound by the movements of the wearer. Also called 'automatic', 'pedometer watch', and 'jerk-winding watch'. Perrelet or Recordon invented the self-winding pocket watch about 1780, and it was made in some numbers by BREGUET. An eccentric weight in the watch, as in a pedometer, oscillated with movements of the wearer and wound the main-spring. LE ROY invented a ROTOR winding system about the same time. The self-winding wrist-watch was invented by an English-man, John Harwood, in 1923, who also invented a system by which the watch strap moved the LUGS of the watch to wind it. In another system, the Rolls by Hatot of Paris, the whole watch oscillated in its case to wind the spring. Currently a number of Swiss factories make only self-winding watches, mostly with rotors which wind when turning in either direction and have a clutch to prevent overwinding. An automatic watch is more accurate than an orthodox one because the mainspring is kept at a more constant tension. There are usually 40 to 50 hours reserve power. Some have UP-AND-DOWN DIALS. The button is for hand setting only.

Sermon Glass   A SAND-GLASS once used on pulpits to time sermons. Loquacious clerics in full spate would sometimes say, 'Let us take another glass . . .'

Serpentine Hand   Clock minute hand which is wavy instead of straight. Introduced about the middle of the eighteenth century.

Set Hands   The clutch mechanism in every timepiece that allows the hands to be set to a new time without damaging the MOVEMENT.

Set in Beat   *See* **Out of Beat.**

Seth Thomas   American clockmaking pioneer born in Wolcott, Connecticut, in 1785. Joined TERRY and Hoadley after being apprenticed as a carpenter and joiner, afterwards making a fortune on his own with factories producing clocks, brass and wire. Set up Seth Thomas Clock Co. in 1859 in Plymouth. Perfected the SHELF CLOCK.

Setting-Up   Pre-tensioning a spring, i.e. fixing the lowest tension to which it can run down. In early spring-driven time-pieces, the MAINSPRING could be set up to different tensions to adjust the power output and therefore the timekeeping. With the FUSEE, the mainspring has to be set up to keep the gut taut. STOP WORK is necessary with such mechanisms.

Sextant   An instrument for measuring angles used in NAVIGA-TION for finding LOCAL TIME by star observations. The height of a star is found by turning a knob of the marine sextant so that an image of the star is brought down to the horizon. A scale then gives the angle. The bubble sextant, which has an artificial horizon, is used for aircraft.

Shagreen   Shark skin used for nineteenth century watch cases. Imitated also by other fish skins and leather dyed green.

Sheepshead Clock   A LANTERN CLOCK with a particularly large DIAL, supposed to make it look like a sheep's head.

Shelf Clock   American pendulum clock with a tallish case up to about 4 ft. which stood on a shelf. Some looked like cut down LONG CASE CLOCKS.

Shepherd's Dial   Early kind of portable ALTITUDE SUNDIAL of cylinder shape from which the GNOMON protrudes horizontally. A vertical line on the cylinder, corresponding to the HOURS of the month, is held facing the Sun and end of the shadow shows the hour on a horizontal scale.

Ship's Bell Clock   Clock striking on the ship's bell system (*see* **Ship's Time**). An unusual one was in the Royal withdrawing room at the Festival of Britain. The glass bell was also the clock case.

Ship's Time   Three systems of time are used on board ships. A sailor's day is reckoned from noon and divided into a series of 'watches'. Each is of four hours except the two Dog Watches of two hours each. During a watch the SHIP'S BELL is struck once at the end of the first half hour, twice at the second, up to eight times at the end of the four hours. A passenger's day is a normal 24 hours, as shown on SLAVE CLOCKS on the ship operated from a MASTER CLOCK, which is advanced or retarded at night, according to whether the ship is going west or east, to adjust approximately to LOCAL TIME. The third time reckoning is GREENWICH MEAN TIME shown by the ship's CHRONOMETER. This, compared with local time obtained by a SEXTANT and the NAUTICAL ALMANAC from the Sun, Moon or stars, gives the ship's longitude for navigation.

Shock Absorber   Arrangement to protect the delicate PIVOTS of a jewelled BALANCE WHEEL from damage if a watch is knocked.

157

The JEWELS are carried in special self-centring, spring-loaded seats which will absorb blows from various directions. The first was Breguet's PARACHUTE. Present systems are more precise and efficient.

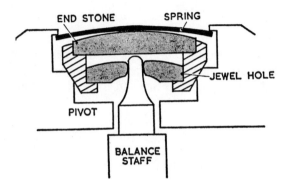

Fig. 24. Shock absorber.

Shortt Clock   The most accurate form of pendulum clock ever made. Invented by W. H. Shortt in 1921 for use as an OBSERVATORY CLOCK. *See* **Free Pendulum Clock.**

Sidereal Clock   Clock keeping SIDEREAL TIME, used in observatories for star observations and TIME DETERMINATIONS. Some clocks show MEAN TIME as well as SIDEREAL.

Sidereal Time   The time of rotation of the Earth as measured from a CLOCK STAR, instead of from the Sun. This is more accurate but ignores daylight, giving a day of 23 hr. 56 min. 4.1 sec. It is thus impractical for ordinary use, but is employed in TIME DETERMINATION. OBSERVATORY CLOCKS are made to show sidereal time. *See* **Nutation, Precession of the Equinox** *and* **Transit Instrument.**

Signatures The actual makers of old clocks and watches engraved their names on the dial and back PLATE. In the eighteenth century, they continued to do so because they were the designers and finishers although much work was put out to makers of parts, called 'chamber masters'. In the late eighteenth and nineteenth centuries more and more clockmakers, including famous ones, bought complete MOVEMENTS and sometimes complete clocks from specialist manufacturers in CLERKENWELL and elsewhere for their regular 'lines' but still signed them. The same makers sometimes supplied to retailers who had *their* names engraved as makers. Some such clocks even bear customers' names. So the true maker is sometimes not the person named on the dial. There may be a punch mark somewhere in the movement revealing the real maker.

Silent Escapement The noisy ticks of the VERGE ESCAPEMENT was an objection to NIGHT CLOCKS, so Joseph KNIBB attached short lengths of springs to the PALLETS to absorb the shock of the CROWN WHEEL and noise. Justin VULLIAMY in mid-eighteenth century, mainly for NIGHT CLOCKS, introduced lengths of taut gut to replace the metal PALLETS. Some modern ALARMS have a form of silencing. The MAGNETIC ESCAPEMENT is also silent.

Silk Suspension Method of suspending a PENDULUM from a loop of silk thread, the PENDULUM rod having a hook at the top. Timekeeping is adjusted by winding up the thread. Often seen in earlier French clocks.

Silvering Matt silver finish of the brass CHAPTER RING of most antique clocks. Before the invention of silvering, about 1660, decorative clock parts and chapter rings were sometimes in solid silver.

Singing Bird Clockwork mechanism with bellows imitating bird songs, usually associated with AUTOMATA of birds. Some

159

are in snuff-boxes, which reveal a miniature 'bird' when opened, others are life-sized 'birds' in cages which move and sing so realistically it is difficult to believe they are not alive. Made by early English clockmakers such as PINCHBECK and later in large numbers from mid-eighteenth century by the Swiss, French and Germans, until the 1920s. Famous makers were the Brugiers family (*c.* 1770–1886), Jacquet-Droz, the Rochat family, Lami, Jean David and Auguste, and the Maillardet brothers, all of Geneva; and the firm of LE ROY, and Blaise Bontemps, of Paris.

Sinking Bowl   Bronze bowl with a hole in it which sinks in a given time when floated in water; used by the Saxons as a WATER CLOCK, or more accurately, a TIMER. Still used today in Algeria to time irrigation of land.

Six Pips   The familiar RADIO TIME SIGNAL originated from a talk on the B.B.C. given by HOPE-JONES on 21 April 1923, the year after the DAYLIGHT SAVING ACT, when he vocalized the last six seconds to the hour. The electrically produced 'pips' started in August 1923. They are correct to within 0.1 sec. and normally within 0.05 sec.

Size   American system of watch measurement originated by A. L. DENNISON, based on thirtieths of an inch. 0 size is the basis, equalling 35/30ths in. 1 size is a thirtieth larger, i.e. 36/30ths, and so on. 1/0 size is a thirtieth smaller, i.e. 34/30ths, and so on. *See* **Ligne.**

Skeleton Clock   Spring-driven clock in which the PLATES, DIAL, and other parts are 'skeletonized', i.e. elaborately pierced. Usually under a glass dome. Very popular from about 1860. Occasionally the MOVEMENTS of weight-driven LONG CASE CLOCKS and REGULATORS were skeletonized (Plate 6).

Skeleton Watch   Watch in which the PLATES or EBAUCHE,

COCKS, BRIDGES, BARREL, DIAL, and so on, are pierced like fretwork. An early version was by Thos. MUDGE, in the eighteenth century. A few skeleton pocket watches are still made in Switzerland.

Skull Watch Watch made in the seventeenth century in the form of a skull, sometimes of silver or wood. Read by opening the jaw. *See* **Mary Queen of Scots' Watch.**

Slave Dial A clock dial in which the hands are operated by an electro-magnet from the electric impulses sent every half minute from a MASTER CLOCK elsewhere. Also called an 'impulse dial'.

Smallest Watch Small watches for their time, such as PURITAN WATCHES, have been made since early days. An amazingly small and complicated RING WATCH was made by John ARNOLD for King George II. He refused to make another for the Empress of Russia. The smallest watch in quantity production is made by Jaeger Le Coultre. The MOVEMENT has 74 parts including 15 jewels and measures just over $\frac{1}{2}$ in. by just under $\frac{1}{8}$ in. In the first half of the nineteenth century, the Swiss made some small watches of pocket watch style, $\frac{1}{2}$ in. and less in diameter, with CYLINDER or LEVER ESCAPEMENTS (Plates 1 *and* 8).

Smith, Sir Alan Gordon (1881–1951) Principal founder of the reborn BRITISH HOROLOGICAL INDUSTRY, who turned his father's jeweller's shop in the Strand, London, into almost an entire clock and watch industry.

Smuggling Watch smuggling is caused by high import duties, taxes, and quotas, which make it profitable. Many thousands of watches are smuggled yearly by well-run organizations into the U.K. from Switzerland and sold by agents in factories and public houses. Many are inferior watches with imitation JEWELS which are in fact dear at the price asked, but others are good.

Diamonds are smuggled out to pay for them. The U.S.A., Italy, India, various countries in Africa, etc., are also badly affected. It is illegal to possess a smuggled watch.

Snail   A cam shaped like a snail's shell. Used particularly for the hook holding the end of the MAINSPRING to the ARBOR of the BARREL, which thus avoids breakage by following the spiral of the spring.

Snailing   Curved lines radiating from the centre of the polished steel winding wheels in a watch, or the steel small end (the 'cap') of a FUSEE, used for decoration.

Solar Dial   The 24-hr. DIAL of a TIME SWITCH or GAS CONTROL-LER which switches street lights on and off and adjusts the switching times according to the time of year. The dial carries two cams to operate the on and off switches and is revolved by a clock. The position of the cams is altered daily by an ingenious automatic indexing arrangement.

Solar Time   Time measured by a SUNDIAL. A solar day is from the Sun's highest point (MERIDIAN) on one day to its meridian on the next. Solar days vary in length throughout the year. To simplify timekeeping, the average solar day over the year, called the 'mean solar day', is taken as a standard and divided into EQUAL HOURS. Mean solar time at Greenwich is GREENWICH MEAN TIME. *See* **Equation of Time.**

Solid Balance   Straightforward BALANCE WHEEL normally made of a single metal, and therefore without BI-METALLIC COMPENSATION. Not a CUT BALANCE. TEMPERATURE COMPENSA-TION is usually effected by making the HAIRSPRING of NIVAROX or a similar alloy.

'Solunar' Dial   Daily tidal times, as shown on some wrist-CHRONOGRAPHS and used in conjunction with 'solunar tables'

(J. Alden Knight) to forecast feeding times of fish and game for sportsmen. Can be set for different places. *See* **Tidal Dial.**

Spade Hand   Hand with an end like the Ace of Spades.

Spandrel   English BRACKET CLOCKS have a circular CHAPTER RING on a square DIAL, the corners of which were at first engraved but very soon were filled with triangular ornaments of cast brass, called 'spandrels'. The earliest, from about 1660, had cherubs' heads and were finely chiselled. Later they became less well finished. The cherub persisted for about 100 years, but many other designs, particularly leaf and scroll, were popular. Brass spandrels were given a coat of GILDING; occasionally they were made entirely of silver (Fig. 19).

Spherical Watch   Probably the earliest form made (*see* **Musk Ball Watch**). Small spherical or BALL WATCHES for women are still made to be used as a FOB WATCH or on a chain round the neck.

Spiral Hairspring   A HAIRSPRING of spiral form. The earliest, of untempered steel, had 1½ to 2 turns; by mid-eighteenth century there were 4 to 5 turns; modern ones have about 12 turns. The inner end is fixed by a collet to the STAFF (axle) of the BALANCE WHEEL. The outer end is fixed to a stud on the BALANCE COCK, or may be curved inwards as an OVERCOIL. *See* **Regulator** *and* **Index.**

Split Seconds   A TIMER with two CENTRE SECONDS HANDS, one over the other, and an extra push button. The main push button starts, stops, and returns both hands to zero. After the hands are started, the second push button will stop the 'split hand' only and when pressed again, cause it to catch up the other hand. Useful for timing both first and second places in athletic events.

Sports Timer A TIMER of pocket watch shape which is calibrated in $\frac{1}{5}$ to $\frac{1}{100}$ sec., for athletics, or in a special way for other sports (*see* **Split Seconds**). For boxing, 3 min. rounds with 1 min. intervals are shown by the minute hand; for football, $\frac{3}{4}$ hr.; for hockey, 35 min. and ice hockey 20 min.; for water polo, 7 min. with an interval of 5 min.; and for yacht races, the 5 min. interval before the starting gun is indicated. With a sculling timer, ten strokes are timed and the hand then indicates the strokes per minute. *See also* **Tachometer, Telemeter** *and* **Chronograph.**

Sports Timing For this, the TIMERS and CHRONOMETERS used are certified. (The BRITISH HOROLOGICAL INSTITUTE checks them for the Auto Cycle Union which controls motor and motorcycle racing and Road Time Trials Association controlling bicycle time trials. The NATIONAL PHYSICAL LABORATORY has more elaborate tests for these and others.) The man who is the TIMEKEEPER usually has to pass tests, also. The Amateur Athletics has carried out such tests at Motspur Park since 1949. Checked over 100 to 220 yards races against a man considered a master timekeeper, a candidate has to score 90, 80 or 70% accuracy to be graded 1st, 2nd or 3rd class. Average reaction time to starting and stopping signals is 0.02 seconds. Actual error depends partly on the form of TIMER used.

Spotting Decoration used for the brass PLATES of clocks and MARINE CHRONOMETERS, used inside watch cases, rows of spots being produced by a small circular polishing tool.

Spring *See* **Mainspring** *and* **Hairspring.**

Spring Detent The now universal DETENT ESCAPEMENT for MARINE CHRONOMETERS, invented by BERTHOUD, ARNOLD and EARNSHAW. The detent or lever which releases the ESCAPE WHEEL is mounted on a spring instead of a PIVOT, which eliminates variations caused by wear of the pivot and the necessity to oil it.

Stackfreed   Device on earliest German watches to improve poor timekeeping. The crude MAINSPRING lost power rapidly as it ran down. To make power output more even, the mainspring also turned a cam, on the edge of which a roller was pressed by a spring. This caused extra friction, which decreased as the mainspring ran down. The turns of the mainspring were also limited by STOP WORK for the same reason.

Stadium Timer   Large TIMER dial, usually operated electrically, for sports audiences. Calibrated according to the sport concerned.

Staff   Watchmaker's name for the axle of the BALANCE.

Stainless Steel   Nickel-chromium steel commonly used for entire watch cases and the backs of ROLLED GOLD or GOLD-PLATED cases, as it resists the acids from the skin.

Standard Time   Time applying in a particular TIME ZONE, or country if this overlaps zones. In Britain, Standard Time is G.M.T. Canada has five standard zones an hour apart as the country spreads over five zones. They are: Atlantic, Eastern, Central, Mountain and Pacific Times.

Star Transit   The time at which a star crosses the MERIDIAN.

Star Wheel   Star-shaped wheel used to give positive movements of CALENDAR and other dials of clocks or watches. A v-shaped spring, called a 'jumper', causes the star wheel to jump swiftly from one indication to the next. *See illustration overleaf.*

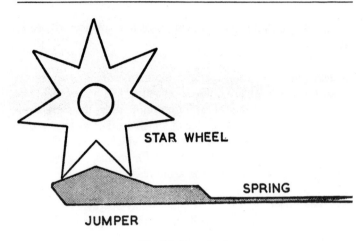

Fig. 25. Star wheel.

Steuart Corrector Arrangement of an electric motor control-led by a pendulum invented by Alexander Steuart to control the public clocks in Edinburgh, the TIME GUN at the Castle, and the TIME BALL on Cotton Hill, from the Royal Observatory at Edinburgh.

'Stopper' Watchmaker's name for a watch that stops at infrequent intervals for reasons difficult to trace.

Stop-Watch A TIMER in pocket watch form for recording time intervals. *See* **Production Timer, Sports Timing** *and* **Split Seconds.**

Stop Work Arrangement to prevent a mainspring from being over-wound, when the spring coils may bind together and stop the timepiece. Used also on very early watches and clocks and on musical boxes to prevent the mainspring from running *down* too much, thus causing bad timekeeping (or slow music).

166

The most common form on the modern watch is the RECOILING CLICK to prevent overwinding.

RECOILING CLICK

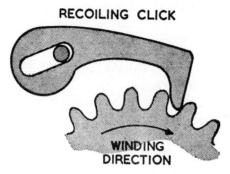

WINDING
DIRECTION

Fig. 26. Stop work.

Strap, Watch A leather strap to hold a watch to the wrist, invented by an Englishman, A. E. Pearson, for soldiers who wanted WRIST-WATCHES during the First World War. An early strap had a leather cup to hold the watch. Then loops were soldered to the watch case to take loops in the strap. LUGS are most common today. A spring-loaded bar between a pair of lugs passes through a loop in the strap. Straps are often padded and have turned-in edges, being sewn with thread or nylon and/or glued. Leathers, pigskin, crocodile and other skins are used as well as fabric and nylon cloth.

Strasbourg Clock Elaborate ASTRONOMICAL and AUTOMATA CLOCK in Strasbourg Cathedral, France, first erected in 1354, reconstructed by Isaac and Josias HABRECHT in 1575, and redesigned and rebuilt by J. R. Schwilgué in 1842. It incorporates a mechanical globe and a mechanical cock that crows three times at noon.

Striking Clock Clock that sounds the hours on a bell or GONG.

167

Very early clocks did this without indicating the time on a dial. The striking TRAIN is separate from the GOING TRAIN of gears, being released by it at the hours by a system of pins and levers incorporating a LOCKING PLATE or RACK. *See* **Chiming Clock.**

Style Another name for GNOMON.

Su Sung's Clock A MONUMENTAL CLOCK made in 1088 by a Chinaman, Su Sung. It had one of the first known ESCAPEMENTS, a water wheel controlled by two steelyards or weigh-bridges. The clock was 30 to 40 ft. high. On top was a huge power-driven ARMILLARY SPHERE of bronze and inside a room with an automatic CELESTIAL GLOBE. A 5-storey pagoda on the front had doors through which JACKS appeared every quarter hour ringing bells and holding tablets to indicate the hours. The clock consumed half a ton of water in 9 hours, and also contained the earliest endless chain, oblique gearing, long transmission shafts, cup bearings, and 'telescope drive'.

Subscription Watch The famous watchmaker BREGUET never made two watches alike except for a series known as 'subscription' which were claimed to be the cheapest very high quality watches made. They were produced in batches and subscribed for in advance. They have large enamelled dials and single hands.

Sully, Henry (1680–1728) Clever but unlucky maker who travelled on the Continent after his apprenticeship and became friendly with Julien LE ROY. He took 60 English watchmakers and their families to Versailles and later St Germain to improve French standards of craftsmanship, but was unlucky financially and in health. Invented the OIL SINK and a marine timekeeper. French revolutionaries removed most of the inscription on his memorial in St Sulpice Church, Paris, which gave him credit for helping the French industry.

Summer Time STANDARD TIME which has been advanced by one hour in the U.K. *See* **Daylight Saving.**

Sun and Moon Watch Watch with an unusual dial, which appeared about 1700. The minute hand is normal. Hours are shown by an image of the Sun travelling round a semicircular slot marked from 6 a.m. to 6 p.m. An image of the Moon follows, showing the hours from 6 p.m. to 6 a.m.

Sun Ray Clock Wall clock with a case like a 'sunburst' with rays of gilded metal, wood, or, in contemporary styles, of wire.

Sundial Method of showing time by shadows cast by the Sun according to its direction (COMPASS SUNDIAL), or height (ALTITUDE SUNDIAL), in the sky. The earliest were probably Egyptian and spread to the Roman Empire (about 290 B.C.) and Grecian Empire. A popular early type was the HEMI-CYCLIUM. England's earliest sundials are Saxon, and on Bewcastle Cross, Cumberland (*c.* A.D. 670), and Kirkdale Church, Yorkshire (*c.* 1060). PORTABLE SUNDIALS were also made from early times. Early sundials showed TEMPORAL HOURS. From mid-fourteenth century they began to show EQUAL HOURS after an Arab mathematician, Abu'l Hassan, calculated that the GNOMON should be parallel to the Earth's axis. After mechanical clocks were introduced, the sundial remained in use as a master by which to set them. During the seventeenth and eighteenth centuries, portable sundials were supplied with the best clocks.

Suspension Flexible or pivoted mounting of a pendulum, usually a SUSPENSION SPRING. Early VERGE clocks had knife edge suspension (like a weighing-machine). SILK SUSPENSION is another form.

Suspension Spring Short length of clock spring on which a

169

pendulum hangs. Invented by Wm. CLEMENT, 1671, or Robert HOOKE earlier.

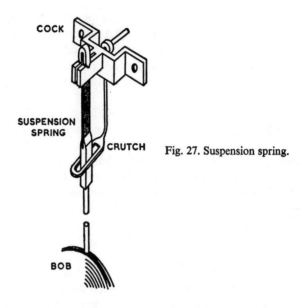

Fig. 27. Suspension spring.

Sweep Seconds   American name for CENTRE SECONDS.

Swiss Horological Industry   Geneva goldsmiths of the sixteenth century were the first Swiss watchmakers and in the next centuries they specialized in ENAMELLED WATCHES. When the Huguenots were driven from France in 1685, many watch-makers went over the mountains into Switzerland. The chief workers were the 'cabinotiers', who turned their own homes into workshops. The Swiss soon adopted the GOING BARREL instead of the FUSEE and mechanization (*see* **Ingold**), particularly in the Neuchatel area, which started them towards becoming the world's biggest and finest watchmakers. Now the industry is divided into four groups under the Swiss Chamber of Horology:

1. The Swiss Watch Federation of over 500 manufacturers and finishers of JEWELLED LEVER WATCHES. 2. Ebauches S.A., a group of 18 factories making parts for jewelled lever watches. 3. Union des Branches Annexes de l'Horologerie, makers of all parts except EBAUCHES. 4. Roscopf Association, 44 factories making cheaper ROSCOPF-type watches. There are several watch-testing stations and compulsory quality control was also introduced in 1962. Output of watches is about 40 million yearly. Jewelled lever travelling and alarm clocks are also made in quantity. The industry is almost entirely in the Valley of the Loire and the Jura Mountains.

Sympathetic Clock Amazing time-controlling arrangement invented by BREGUET in 1805–10. It comprised a clock and watch. The watch was placed in a clip in the clock at night and the clock, at a fixed hour, not only reset the watch to the correct time, but also REGULATED it according to its gaining or losing RATE. This incorporated the principle of feedback, the basis of automation.

Synchronous Clock Electric clock dial operated from the main supply frequency, invented by H. E. Warren of the U.S.A. in 1918. The 'clock' is actually a synchronous electric motor which keeps in step with the generators at the power station, which are themselves kept in step with G.M.T. by a FREQUENCY COMPARISON METER. The frequency in the U.K. is 50 cycles a second and in the U.S.A. 60.

Tabernacle Clock Miniature TOWER CLOCK six to nine inches high, made in the sixteenth and seventeenth centuries. The MOVEMENT was similar to that of a LANTERN CLOCK, but driven by a MAINSPRING and FUSEE instead of a weight.

Table Clock Most common form of early clock of the late sixteenth and seventeenth centuries, being DRUM shaped, or later, square, or hexagonal, with feet. Separate ALARM mechanisms were common on early ones. Hexagonal table clocks, in particular, were made in Germany well into the eighteenth century (Plate 3).

Tachometer   Scale sometimes combined with a wrist-CHRONO-GRAPH, to show speed over a given distance, such as one mile or one kilometre marked on the dial. Timing a motor-car, say, over this distance records the speed in m.p.h. or k.p.h.

Tact Watch   Montre à tact made by BREGUET for blind people. The watch cover had fixed studs to mark the hours, and a movable pointer, which, when turned clockwise by the wearer, was stopped at the correct time. It was a cheaper alternative to a REPEATER.

Talking Clock   Clock which 'speaks' the time, the most common being the telephone voice TIM. The earliest were made about 1914, comprising a clock MOVEMENT, speech record on a band, acoustic head, gramophone needle, and horn.

Tambour (or Tambourine Watch)   Another name for a DRUM WATCH or canister watch, the case being like a round tin with the perforated LID and the MOVEMENT hinged to it.

Tape Chronograph   Instrument for comparing the RATES of clocks, CHRONOMETERS, and STAR TRANSITS. In the simplest instrument, a timekeeping mechanism moves a paper tape under two pens which draw straight lines on the paper. Each pen can be given a jerk by an electro-magnet connected to a clock or TRANSIT INSTRUMENT. Therefore humps in the lines compare the rates. More elaborate versions, such as the Belin chronograph, are used by observatories.

172

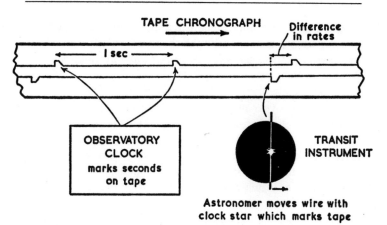

TAPE CHRONOGRAPH

Difference
in rates

1 sec

OBSERVATORY
CLOCK
marks seconds
on tape

TRANSIT
INSTRUMENT

Astronomer moves wire with
clock star which marks tape

Fig. 28. Tape chronograph.

Fig. 29. Tavern clock.

173

Tavern Clock   Another name for a COACHING CLOCK or ACT OF PARLIAMENT CLOCK (although they were in use well before the TAXES ON TIMEKEEPERS). *See illustration previous page.*

Taxes on Timekeepers   In 1797, William Pitt introduced a tax of 5 shillings a year on every clock, 10 shillings each on gold watches, and 2*s* 6*d* on silver watches. Clock and watch makers had to take out licences. This increased the popularity of the tavern clock, which became known as the ACT OF PARLIAMENT CLOCK. At the same time there was a 'plate tax' existing on gold and silver watch cases. Both Acts were repealed in 1798.

Telemeter   Scale sometimes combined with a wrist-CHRONOGRAPH to record the distance of an event seen and heard, such as a thunderstorm. The recording hand is released when lightning is seen and stopping when the thunder is heard, the hand then indicating the distance away of the storm.

Telephone Timer   A special ELAPSED TIME INDICATOR for use with telephones on the Subscriber Trunk Dialling system. Some 'ping' every three minutes and give the cost of the call.

Telleruhr   Literally a 'plate clock'. Made in the sixteenth and seventeenth centuries in Germany (particularly in Augsburg) and Austria. Usually hung on the wall but occasionally stood on a pedestal. The flat metal DIAL with elaborately shaped edges has a REPOUSSÉ centre and sometimes a silver or pewter CHAPTER RING. In some, the short pendulum hangs over the front of the dial. The hands are usually elaborately pierced. *See* **Trophy Clock.**

Tell-Tale Clock   Alternative name for a WATCHMAN'S CLOCK.

Temperature Compensation   Method of avoiding timekeeping variations (TEMPERATURE ERROR) at different temperatures,

174

which affect PENDULUMS, BALANCE AND SPRINGS, QUARTZ CRYSTALS, and most other time standards. COMPENSATION PENDULUMS are designed to keep the lengths invariable. A balance and a hairspring are affected separately, and differently, by temperature changes, which is a complication. HARRISON first applied compensation to hairsprings—by employing an arrangement like GRIDIRON PENDULUM to vary the tension of CYLINDRICAL HAIRSPRINGS; then by developing a COMPENSATION CURB for spiral springs. Many developments have been made in COMPENSATION BALANCES for use with hairsprings of differing metals and alloys.

Temperature Error Timekeeping error caused by variations in temperature. A PENDULUM with a steel rod will expand in length and become slower by $2\frac{1}{2}$ sec. a day for a rise of $10°$F ($5\frac{1}{2}°$C). A COMPENSATION PENDULUM can eliminate this error. The effect is more complicated with a BALANCE AND SPRING. For the same temperature rise, a brass balance wheel will expand and swing slower by about 5 sec. a day; much more important, the spring will become weaker and lose 1 min. a day. So the balance and spring together lose 65 sec. a day for a rise of $10°$F. A good COMPENSATION BALANCE with special hairspring commonly reduces this error to $\frac{1}{50}$ sec. per day for a $1°$C rise in TIMEKEEPING TRIALS.

Temporal Hours Before the fourteenth century, when there was hardly any artificial illumination, daylight was split into a number of hours, usually 12, and so was the night. A daylight hour was therefore different from a night hour and both varied at different times of the year, but not by much in the Mediterranean areas where most early civilizations thrived. Early sundials show temporal hours. *See* **Mean Time, Equal Hours** *and* **Japanese Clocks.**

Testing *See* **Rating Certificate, Timekeeping Trials, Kew 'A' Certificate** *and* **Quality Standards.**

Thermal Dial   Used on a TIME SWITCH to make or break electric contacts at a given time *or* at a preset temperature.

Thin Long Case Clock   A LONG CASE CLOCK 6 ft. or more high with a trunk only about 8 in. wide. Some are eighteenth century, but these cases were also made from about 1840 to take the MOVEMENTS of LANTERN CLOCKS, usually with BOB PENDULUM and ALARM. Such lantern clocks originally had arched dials and spiked feet.

Thinnest Watch   Thin watches are elegant and fashionable. They were made as early as the start of the eighteenth century by Daniel QUARE. The thinnest in quantity production is 1.18 mm. thick (slightly over $\frac{4}{100}$ in.). A SELF-WINDING WATCH only 2.5 mm. ($\frac{1}{10}$ in.) thick is also made in Switzerland. Extra thin movements are sometimes made into COIN WATCHES.

Thirty-Hour Clock   Clock which runs at least 30 hr. at one winding. Intended to be wound daily. A few early LANTERN CLOCKS ran for only 12 hr. or so. Later clocks went for EIGHT DAYS or more, and cheaper ones, 30 hr. The principle applies today for clocks. Some watches will run as long as 45 hr. at a winding. This also improves timekeeping as the MAINSPRING POWER is then more constant when the watch is wound daily.

Thousand-Day Clock   Small, battery-operated pendulum clock with TRANSISTOR switching which runs for 1,000 days on one cell.

Tic Tac Escapement   A small ANCHOR ESCAPEMENT which extends over only two teeth of the ESCAPE WHEEL. Used on French and some early English clocks with BOB PENDULUMS.

Tick   Sound made by the release and arrest of a TRAIN of gears by the ESCAPEMENT, made up by as many as 40 different sounds in a watch. Ticks vary from 'tocks' because alternate PALLETS arrest the ESCAPE WHEEL and different parts of the MOVEMENT resonate. The sound of a tick lasts about 15 MILLISECONDS.

Tick Amplifier The sound of a watch tick can indicate many different faults. Watch repairers sometimes use amplifiers to diagnose them.

Ticket Clock Rather like a circular CARRIAGE CLOCK, but shows the time in figures on celluloid tickets, of which there are two sets, one above the other, for hours and minutes. The tickets are like leaves of a cylindrical book which flip round at the minutes and hours. Invented in 1903. Also called a 'flick leaf clock' or 'Plato clock'.

Fig. 30. Ticket clock.

Tidal Dial Indication on some eighteenth century LONG CASE CLOCKS of high and low tides, often shown on the MOON DIAL. Another version was a rising and falling plate representing the sea, operated by a cam, invented by James Ferguson. They were useful in times when rivers and coastal waters were the principal means of transport. Tidal dials on modern TIME SWITCHES control the flow of sewages or factory effluent into the sea by opening a valve when the tide goes out.

Tide The Saxons divided a day into eight tides, shown by their SUNDIALS. We still use 'noontide' and 'eventide'. The tides were: Morgan 4.30 a.m.–7.30 a.m.; Daeg-mael 7.30 a.m.– 10.30 a.m.; Mid-dag 10.30 a.m.–1.30 p.m.; Afanverth dagr 1.30 p.m.–4.30 p.m.; Mid-aften 4.30 p.m.–7.30 p.m.; Ondverth nott 7.30 p.m.–10.30 p.m.; Mid-niht 10.30 p.m.–1.30 a.m.; Ofanverth nott 1.30 a.m.–4.30 a.m.

TIM The SPEAKING CLOCK of the British Post Office which speaks the exact time when 'TIM' is dialled by the telephone and is accurate to 0.1 sec. It was inaugurated in 1936. The apparatus is controlled by a FREE PENDULUM and the voice announcements are built up from a series of recordings on glass discs. Paris was the first city to have a speaking clock, in 1933. The latest models are controlled by QUARTZ CRYSTAL CLOCKS.

Time No one knows exactly what time is. It is a concept of mind, representing a change from order to disorder. It is not absolute. According to the Theory of Relativity (Einstein) the RATE of a clock depends on the situation of the observer. In practice this means that a clock in an artificial satellite approaching the speed of light goes at a slower rate measured from the Earth than measured from the satellite. Passage of time is measured by referring to a recurring phenomenon, such as the rotation of the Earth, vibration of a PENDULUM, BALANCE, QUARTZ CRYSTAL, MOLECULE or ATOM. Living things have a built-in 'HUMAN CLOCK'. Two kinds of time are in ordinary use: (1) Time of day and (2) Duration of time interval. For (1), rotation of the Earth has to be used. For (2), ATOMIC TIME is more accurate. It would be more practical to base both on Atomic Time for convenience.

Time Ball The world's first accurate TIME SIGNAL, which was installed at GREENWICH OBSERVATORY in 1833 by John Pond for shipping in the Pool of London. The ball was a wooden frame 5 ft. in diameter, covered with leather. It was wound halfway up to the top of a mast on the north-east turret, at 12.58, and dropped down the 15 ft. mast at exactly 1 p.m. by a trigger release. After 1852 the ball was released automatically by an electric signal from an OBSERVATORY CLOCK. Time balls became popular and were erected in the Strand, London (for CHRONO-METER makers) and at Deal, Devonport, Portsmouth, Portland (for shipping), and elsewhere. The present Greenwich ball is of aluminium on a 30 ft. mast and is still operated, but by the National Maritime Museum. Superseded by TIME SIGNALS.

Time Determination This is the duty of the ROYAL GREENWICH OBSERVATORY in Britain and the National Bureau of Standards in the U.S.A. It means determining exact points in time as accurately as possible for TIME DISTRIBUTION. The fundamental unit of time is the period of time the Earth takes to rotate on its axis, which is a day. This can be measured by timing the Sun from noon on one day to noon on the next, as with a SUNDIAL, but the days are found to vary in length (*see* **Solar Time**). It is more accurate to observe a CLOCK STAR instead, to obtain SIDEREAL TIME. This is done by taking an observation with a TRANSIT INSTRUMENT and comparing the going of the Earth with the going of the OBSERVATORY CLOCKS by means of a TAPE CHRONOGRAPH. Clocks have proved to be the more accurate timekeepers, showing up wobbling (NUTATION) and other irregularities in the Earth's rotation. Mean sidereal time is sidereal time corrected for these irregularities and can be converted to mean solar time for general use. However, time is now even more accurately determined from observation of the Earth's orbit, which provides EPHEMERIS TIME and is converted to mean solar time for TIME DISTRIBUTION for public consumption (Fig. 28).

179

Time Distribution After TIME DETERMINATION, the ROYAL GREENWICH OBSERVATORY distributes time to the Post Office, B.B.C., NATIONAL PHYSICAL LABORATORY, and other main users. Earlier in the century other distributors of time were the Post Office (by their CHRONOGRAPHER); and the Standard Time Co. of London; the Self-Winding Clock Co., of New York, and Normallzeit Gesellschaft, of Berlin, who set up electric wires to railway stations, CHRONOMETER makers, and elsewhere, through which a synchronizing signal at a certain time forcibly corrected clocks on the spot.

Time Gun Gun fired as a TIME SIGNAL, such as that on Edinburgh Castle. Not as accurate as a TIME BALL because of the sound delay. The earliest were fired by the Sun's rays to give a SOLAR TIME signal.

Time Lock Special safe or strong-room lock that enables the door to be opened only after a certain time. Invented by James Sargeant in the U.S.A. in 1872. The time lock is wound with a clock key when the door is open and set for a certain period of time. When the door is shut and the bolts thrown, the time lock blocks the bolt mechanism until the time has elapsed. Usually two or more clock mechanisms are used in case one should stop.

Time Recorder Clock which gives a permanent record of certain events. The first was Whitehurst's WATCHMAN'S CLOCK. In 1885, an American, Bundy, invented a clock that printed the time when keys were inserted, to 'clock in' employees. The modern factory version is controlled by a MASTER CLOCK and automatically stamps cards with the time at which they are inserted, being used for job costing as well as employee control. Another version used on lorries records the periods of time that they are in motion.

180

Time Signal   Indication of a specific time, usually by a visual or aural signal. *See* **Radio Time Signal, Time Ball, TIM** *and* **Time Gun.**

Time Stamp   A rubber date stamp which also prints a dial and hand showing the time of stamping. It incorporates a timepiece. Some have DIGITAL INDICATION. Can be self-contained or be controlled by a MASTER CLOCK.

Time Switch   Electric or mechanical switch operated by a clock mechanism, used for street lighting (usually with a SOLAR DIAL), factory heating, shop window lighting, radio switching, refrigerator switching, time bombs, etc. *See* **Gas Controller.**

Time Zone   If countries employed LOCAL TIMES, time of day would change with the smallest journey east or west. So in 1884 the world was split into 24 time zones of 15° each. The principal one is $7\frac{1}{2}$ each side of Greenwich to which G.M.T. applies. Each zone successively west became an hour earlier and each zone east an hour later. The centre of the zone on the side of the world opposite Greenwich is the DATE LINE. Countries which fall in two zones declare for one or the other, and big countries may have several STANDARD TIMES. There are also other local variations including DAYLIGHT SAVING. *See* **World Time Dial.**

Timer   A pocket watch, or clock, for measuring short time intervals. The earliest, in the eighteenth century, had an arm which pressed against a wheel in the mechanism to stop it. The first watch in which the hand returned to zero was shown by Nicole and Capt at the London Exhibition of 1862. The push button of a pocket timer is pressed once to start the hands, again to stop them, and a third time to return them to zero. The accuracy depends on the BEAT of the balance. One beating

$\frac{1}{5}$ sec. is accurate approximately to that. For greater accuracy, balances beating up to $\frac{1}{100}$ sec., and occasionally more, are used. *See* **Sports Timer, Pulse Meter, Tachometer, Telemeter, Split Seconds Timer, Decimal Timer, Production Timer** *and* **Chronograph.** A clock timer can also have hands that return to zero. *See* **Process Timer, Interval Timer, Elapsed Time Indicator** *and* **Time Switch.** For sportsmen, skin divers, airline pilots and others needing to judge time intervals, there is an accurate watch with a CENTRE SECONDS HAND, which has an extra set of minute markings reading *anti-clockwise* on the BEZEL. The bezel can be rotated and is turned so that the time interval, say 20 min., is opposite the minute hand. The minute hand then moves towards zero on the bezel, always showing the remaining minutes. If the bezel is set opposite the centre seconds hand, remaining seconds are indicated.

Timekeeper Any form of TIMEPIECE, CLOCK, CHRONOMETER, TIME SWITCH, or other device showing time of day. Also a person responsible for timekeeping for any purpose such as recording times in sports events, or at a factory. *See* **Sports Timing.**

Timekeeping Trials Special competitions for performance of timekeepers under strict conditions, including tests in differing positions, ovens, and refrigerators. In the eighteenth and nineteenth centuries the most important ones were run by the ROYAL GREENWICH OBSERVATORY for MARINE CHRONOMETERS. Today the most important trials are controlled by the Geneva and Neuchatel Observatories, and the prizes are monopolized by Swiss makers and ADJUSTERS.

Timepiece Strictly, a clock or watch showing time of day only and not striking or chiming.

Timing Machine Another name for a RATE RECORDER.

Timing Screws   Screws around the rim of a CUT BALANCE. Also called 'MEAN TIME screws'. There are four to adjust the RATE, since the balance swings slower when they are screwed outwards. They are placed at 90° to each other starting from the ends of the arm of the balance. Other screws in the rim are adjusted for TEMPERATURE COMPENSATION and POISE (Fig. 5).

Timing Washers   Tiny washers placed under the screws in the rim of a BALANCE to adjust the RATE at which it swings and also to correct POISE errors.

Ting Tang   Most ancient form of chime on two bells, sometimes struck by two QUARTER BOYS giving one blow on each at quarter past, doing this twice at half past, three times at a quarter to, and four before the hour. The first bell has a higher note. HAMPTON COURT CLOCK is ting tang. The system is also used in REPEATER WATCHES.

Tipsy Key   Winding key for watches with a ratchet so that it could not be turned backwards. Also called a 'BREGUET key'.

Tompion, Thomas (1639–1713)   Usually regarded as the most famous of all English clock and watchmakers. Born at Ickwell Green, Northill, Bedfordshire, and trained as a blacksmith, but went to London and became a clockmaker, setting up at 'The Dial and Three Crowns', Water Lane, Fleet Street. Collaborated with Dr HOOKE. Made the first clocks for GREENWICH OBSERVATORY in 1676, the first EQUATION CLOCK, now in the ROYAL COLLECTION, and a YEAR CLOCK as well as the 'RECORD' TOMPION for King William III. Invented a forerunner of the CYLINDER ESCAPEMENT for watches with BARLOW and Wm. Houghton. Became famous in his own time, particularly for watches, of which he produced about 5,500. He made about 650 clocks and also barometers and other instruments. Buried in

183

Westminster Abbey. Succeeded by George GRAHAM. *See* **Bath Clock** *and* Plate 1.

Torsion Pendulum Pendulum that twists on its SUSPENSION SPRING instead of swinging to and fro. Has a slow BEAT, therefore consuming small power so that it is used for FOUR HUNDRED DAY CLOCKS. Invented by Robert Leslie in 1793. Also used in the ATMOS CLOCK.

Tortoise Clock Bowl of water, with hours marked round the rim, in which a metal 'tortoise' floats, to indicate the time. The tortoise is moved round the edge by a magnet turned by clock-work in the base. Invented by GROLLIER. Should be 'turtle clock'! A recent version has a duck in a tiny pond. Also called a 'magnetic clock'.

Tourbillon A watch ESCAPEMENT has POSITIONAL ERRORS. To even out some of these, and improve the RATE, BREGUET invented in 1801 an arrangement for pocket watches in which the entire escapement was mounted on a platform which revolved, usually once a minute, which he called a 'tourbillon'. *See* **Karrusel.**

Tower Clock General name for a large public clock, although many early ones were in the body of churches, not in the tower or turret. First made in the thirteenth century (*see* **Salisbury Cathedral Clock**). The frames were then heavy wrought-iron cages which degenerated to BIRDCAGE and BEDPOST forms. Others had a VERTICAL FRAME. The FLAT BED form, invented in France, is now universal. Most modern tower clocks have a GRAVITY ESCAPEMENT, a LONG PENDULUM and AUTOMATIC WINDING, which avoids a long chute for the weights and the need for a CLOCK WINDER. Some are electric, operated from a MASTER CLOCK; others are SYNCHRONOUS electric, although this is not ideal for public clocks because such clocks stop during power cuts. Also called 'turret clock'.

Tower of Babel Clock   Famous ROLLING BALL CLOCK representing the famous tower, made by Hans Schlottheim for Emperor Rudolf II between 1595 to 1604. A crystal ball ran round a spiral track in a minute to unlock the ESCAPEMENT and was restored to the top by a spring-operated conveyor belt.

Train   Series of engaging gears as used in a timepiece; thus timekeeping train, striking train, and chiming train. The gear ratio is very high, being stepped up in mechanical clocks and stepped down in SYNCHRONOUS. A watchmaker identifies a train by the number of ticks per hour (the BEAT), men's watches usually having an '18,000 train'. Also referred to as 'a count of 18,000'.

Transistor   Miniature electronic switch replacing the mechanical switch in some battery-operated clocks and watches. *See* **Electronic Watch** *and* **Clock.**

Transit Instrument   Special telescope rigidly fixed in an east–west direction, but capable of being swung north–south. It is adjusted to point to a CLOCK STAR each time the Earth rotates. Hence intervals between seeing the same star are 24 hours of SIDEREAL TIME. The astronomer turns a handwheel to move a 'wire' (actually made from spider's web) across the eyepiece in time with the apparent star movement (Fig. 28). This operates electric contacts which make blips on the moving paper tape of a TAPE CHRONOGRAPH, which also records seconds from the OBSERVATORY CLOCK for comparison. Very accurate observations can be taken of some clock stars by an instrument called the 'photo zenith tube', which is connected to the observatory's SIDEREAL CLOCK and photographs star transits and clock records.

Travelling Clock   Spring-driven non-pendulum clock for travelling. Formerly a CARRIAGE CLOCK which fitted into a special case, or a SEDAN CLOCK. Now a CALOTTE and usually an alarm.

Travelling Watch   Large watch for carriage use (Plate 7). Also called a CARRIAGE CLOCK.

Trophy Clock   Another name for PLATE CLOCK or TELLERUHR, as these had name plates on each side of the dial surround for engraving, when used as prizes in Germany.

Trumpeter Clock   Of similar origin to the CUCKOO CLOCK but the bellows blow trumpets instead of cuckoo notes. Some operate drums as well at the hours.

Tubular Chime   Chime on lengths of tube in a LONG CASE CLOCK.

Tulip Decoration   Decoration, such as finials and ENGRAVING on English clock MOVEMENTS and CASES in the seventeenth and early eighteenth centuries, often included tulips because of the Dutch influence.

'Tulip' Tompion   Famous GRANDE SONNERIE bracket clock made by THOMAS TOMPION about 1680 and so called because the FINIALS on top of the case are like tulips.

Turns   Elementary form of lathe used by watch and clock-makers for centuries. It comprises two fixed points, the 'centres', between which the work is fixed. A bow of cane rotates the work, the gut 'string' being given a turn round it. The watch-maker holds his cutting tool with one hand and 'bows' with the other. Very accurate. Almost entirely displaced by the watch-maker's lathe, except in non-industrial countries.

Turret Clock   Another name for a TOWER CLOCK.

Two-Seconds Pendulum   A pendulum BEATING two seconds, which is about 13 ft. 4 in. long. Thomas TOMPION used them in his clocks for GREENWICH OBSERVATORY. B. L. VULLIAMY made a number of clocks with them from about 1816 including those at Horse Guards Parade; Hampton Court; the Cremille (Victualling Yard), Plymouth; Christ Church, Oxford; and Basingstoke Parish Church and Town Hall. Clocks by other makers with 2-seconds pendulums are 'BIG BEN'; St Paul's Cathedral; Birmingham University; Lisburn Cathedral, Co. Down; and over a dozen more over the country. *See* **Long Pendulum.**

Unbreakable Glass   A watch 'glass' made of Perspex, Plexiglas, or other plastics material. *See* **Glass.**

Uniform Time   Time which has been corrected for *all* known irregularities. *See* **Universal Time, Ephemeris Time, Time Determination.**

Universal Clock   A WORLD CLOCK or world time clock.

Universal Sundial   Most SUNDIALS are designed to work only in one latitude. A universal one can be adjusted to any latitude.

Universal Time   Time calculated from the rotation of the Earth (i.e. GREENWICH MEAN TIME) but corrected for certain irregularities, including movement of the Earth's axis and NUTATION. Adopted internationally in 1950 as the basis for civil timekeeping, navigating, and surveying, although it is not absolutely uniform. *See* **Uniform Time** *and* **Time Determination.**

Universal Time Dial   Alternative name for WORLD TIME DIAL. Watches showing time over the world are made for airline pilots and travellers. Some have two dials side by side and the hands can be set to show times in two different places.

Up-and-Down Dial   Dial which shows how much a MAINSPRING is wound. Used on MARINE CHRONOMETERS and some AUTOMATIC WATCHES.

U.S.A. Horological Industry   First American clockmakers were European immigrants, one of the earliest being Wm. Davis who arrived in Boston in 1683. New England States led the way, particularly Connecticut, where Daniel Burnap, Eli TERRY, Seth THOMAS, Elias Hoodley, Chauncy Jerome worked. Main town centres were Plymouth, Winstead, WATERBURY and Bristol, where Elias Ingraham had his workshop. Most famous Massachusetts clockmakers were the Willard family, who developed the BANJO CLOCK. In Pennsylvania, David Rittenhouse (b. 1732) made fine COMPLICATED CLOCKS and mathematical instruments. Mass-production methods and the making of watches by machine were pioneered in the U.S.A., which was first with cheap watches. American watch and clock companies now also have factories in Britain (two), Switzerland, Germany and Japan. Output of watches is 9.2% of the world total. Produced the first ELECTRIC and ELECTRONIC WATCHES.

Vase Clock   A French clock shaped like a vase in which clockwork moves a REVOLVING BAND around the rim to indicate the time.

Velvet Dial   Early Dutch clock style of a metal (sometimes silver) CHAPTER RING on a velvet background. Employed on the first pendulum clock made for HUYGENS.

Verge Escapement   Earliest mechanical clock ESCAPEMENT, comprising a wheel shaped like a king's crown (and called the 'crown wheel'), the teeth of which are released by two PALLETS on an ARBOR (axle) which carries a FOLIOT (Fig. 12). Probably invented in the thirteenth century and used in watches with a

188

BALANCE WHEEL to the eighteenth, and as late as mid-nineteenth century in JAPANESE CLOCKS.

Vertical Frame One of the earliest forms of construction of large church or TOWER CLOCKS in England. The wheels are arranged in a vertical line. All originally had VERGE and FOLIOT escapements. The only one in original condition is the COTEHELE CLOCK. Others with iron frames are at Marston Magna, Sydling St Nicholas, Tytherington, EXETER CATHEDRAL, Ottery St Mary, and Castle Combe. There are two with wooden frames, at Leintwardine in Bedfordshire, and Sharnbrooke in Bedfordshire.

Victoria and Albert Museum Collection The development of decoration is shown by clocks and watches made from 1500 to mid-nineteenth century, in the Department of Metalwork. They include the earliest dated English clock—a BRACKET CLOCK signed FRANCOY NOWE, 1588, and a very large collection of watches. A collection of clocks in the Department of Woodwork illustrates their history as domestic furniture.

Vienna Regulator Weight-driven wall clock with PENDULUM and glass fronted and sided case, made in Austria and Germany. Not strictly a REGULATOR. First made in the early nineteenth century in Vienna and called 'laternuhr' (LANTERN CLOCK) because of the case. These had SECONDS PENDULUMS. Later, ¾-seconds pendulums were used and, with these, the SECONDS HAND does not in fact record seconds.

Virgule Escapement Watch ESCAPEMENT invented about 1750, with similar layout to the CYLINDER ESCAPEMENT, but not so popular.

Vulliamy, Benjamin Lewis (1780–1854) Maker of fine clocks and ROYAL CLOCKMAKER, many by him being in the ROYAL

COLLECTION. Tendered for the making of 'BIG BEN'. Claimed to have invented the BEAT PLATE. Converted many earlier clocks to LEVER ESCAPEMENT, which upset antiquarians.

Waggon Spring Clock   A clock which has a heavy leaf spring, like a half-elliptic road spring of a motor-car, instead of a clock spring, to drive it. The spring is fixed across the bottom of the case. Invented by an American, Joseph Ives, about 1818, and only made in the U.S.A.

Wallace Collection   Famous art collection in Hertford House, Manchester Square, London, which includes some fine French clocks.

Wandering Hour Dial   Seventeenth century watch dial without hands. There is a semi-circular slot marked 0–I–II–III–IV along the bottom edge for quarter hours, and 0 to 60 along the top edge for minutes. An appropriate numeral indicating the hour moves around this slot (Plate 7). Similar to NIGHT CLOCK dial.

Watch   The watch or 'portable clock' became possible when the MAINSPRING was invented to replace the WEIGHT. Earliest were probably Italian, but the only survivors are German of about 1540 and French of 1551. These were ball shaped (wrongly called NUREMBERG EGGS), but were soon displaced by drum-shaped or oval ones of about 2 in. diameter. They had VERGE ESCAPEMENTS with DUMBELL BALANCE or BALANCE WHEEL. Iron or steel was used for construction before about 1560 and brass afterwards. Early German watches had STACKFREEDS; English and French had FUSEES. These were worn on a cord round the neck. After the long waistcoat was popularized in 1675, watches went into waistcoat pockets. The BALANCE SPRING was incorporated in most watches after 1700 making them more accurate and encouraging minute hands. The CYLINDER ESCAPEMENT replaced the VERGE for about 150 years and encouraged seconds hands. LEVER ESCAPEMENTS came into general use after about 1825 until today almost all watches have them. The rate of manufacture was stepped up by the LEPINE CALIBRE and of cheap watches by the methods of JAPY, ROSKOPF, and WATERBURY, until today watches are produced by semi-automatic processes in many tens of millions a year. The WRIST-WATCH is comparatively recent, having become popular only in the last 50 years. An average wrist-watch has about 130 parts which require about 1,400 machining operations in manufacture. *See* **Thinnest Watch** *and* **Smallest Watch.**

Watch Paper Printed or otherwise decorated paper or cambric placed in the back of the PAIR CASE of a watch to prevent chafing. Nearly all watchmakers had their own designs, which included pictures of beauties of the time, EQUATION OF TIME tables, advertisements, mottoes, etc.

Watch Timer An instrument, the RATE RECORDER; or a skilled man, the watch ADJUSTER.

Watch Train An old name for the series of gears responsible for timekeeping of a *clock*, i.e. the GOING TRAIN.

Watchmaker Originally a craftsman who made watches and clocks—the timekeeping part of a clock was then also called 'the watch'. Now a repairer or retailer.

Watchman's Clock Clock to indicate the time at which a night watchman makes his rounds. Invented by Whitehurst of Derby in 1750, whose version had a large rotating disc with pegs round its edge. The watchman struck a lever which pushed in a peg at the time of his visit. In the modern version the watch-man carries a small TIME RECORDER. There are keys chained in the places he must visit. On his rounds he inserts each key and turns it, which gives a time indication and the key number on a paper tape sealed in the recorder.

Water Clock   The earliest were Egyptian stone bowls with sloping sides and with a leak hole near the bottom. After filling, the decreasing water level inside shows the passing hours. Different scales are for the different TEMPORAL HOURS of different months. Introduced into Rome and Greece B.C. and gradually made more and more elaborate in the early centuries A.D., with floats that moved, figures pointing to scales, and mechanisms striking bells, but not much improved in accuracy. Reached its culmination in the elaborate clock of SU SUNG in China. *See* **Sinking Bowl.**

Waterbury Watch   One of the first cheap watches, made in the U.S.A. from 1880 to 1898. Several ingenious but practical models even included a TOURBILLON. The time it took to wind a Waterbury used to be a Music Hall joke.

Waterproof   An unsealed watch case 'breathes', drawing in air when cold and expelling it when warm. It may draw in perspiration from the wrist or moisture from the air, which is deposited on steel parts and rusts them. A water-sealed case prevents this and also stops hairs and dust (which can be harder than steel) being drawn in and forming a grinding paste with the oil. The first waterproof pocket watch was the EXPLORER'S WATCH and first waterproof wrist-watch one by Rolex. Most 'waterproof' watches are not intended to be used under water and should be called 'water resistant'. Special ones are made for skin diving and tested to the equivalent of 600 ft. and more. Waterproofing can deteriorate through wear and non-replacement of sealing washers. Even a truly waterproof watch may show a milky moisture deposit on the glass in cold weather from air sealed in it. The main sealing places are at the back of the case, the glass, and the winding button. *See* **Diver's Watch.**

192

Webster Collection   Fine collection of clocks and watches including many FORM WATCHES, broken up and sold on the death of Percy Webster, their owner, in 1954.

Weight   Every mechanical clock before about 1450 was driven by a weight hanging from a rope wound round a drum or BARREL. Weights have continued in use to the present time because they give more even power than springs. Early weights were of stone. Later, cast iron and lead (enclosed in brass until the end of the eighteenth century for the best clocks) were used.

Wells Cathedral Clock   Large iron clock made before 1392 and now in the SCIENCE MUSEUM, London, which strikes (being controlled by one of the earliest LOCKING PLATES) and chimes. Converted to ANCHOR AND PENDULUM in the seventeenth century. Both Wells and SALISBURY clocks, which are very similar, may have been made under the instruction of Bishop Erghum, from Bruges, who was at Salisbury from 1375–85 (*see* **Lightfoot**). The clock once operated JACK BLANDIFER and the other AUTOMATA in the cathedral but was removed in 1835 in favour of a new MOVEMENT.

Westminster Chime   Familiar chime of the WESTMINSTER PALACE CLOCK ('Big Ben') which was taken from the fifth bar of Handel's *Messiah*, 'I know that my Redeemer liveth', and modified by Mr Crotch and Dr Jowett originally for St Mary's Church, Cambridge, in 1793-4.

Westminster Palace Clock   The clock popularly known as 'BIG BEN', in a tower of the Palace of Westminster, the official name for the Houses of Parliament. The first clock there was in a tower built about 1365. It struck a great bell every hour. This was followed by another in a new tower after the Commonwealth, striking on GREAT TOM. When the tower of the

193

present Westminster Palace was nearly finished in 1844, the architect, Sir Charles Barry, wrote to B. L. VULLIAMY for plans of a clock. Another prominent maker, E. J. Dent, objected and asked also to be allowed to tender. It was then decided to ask the Astronomer Royal, G. B. AIRY, to draw up a specification, and submit it to Vulliamy, Dent, and Whitehurst of Derby, for tender. Most clockmakers thought Airy's condition, that the first blow of each hour should be accurate to a second, impossible for so huge a clock. They included Vulliamy, who withdrew. Dent won the contract and Airy asked Lord GRIMTHORPE to supervise the making of the clock. Grimthorpe, a ruthless and sharp-tongued lawyer, was also a brilliant amateur clockmaker. During the 15 years of design and construction, Dent died and his stepson Frederick Dent was appointed after a legal battle. There were wars with the architect, Astronomer Royal (who resigned from the committee), bell founders, authorities, and other clockmakers; there were intrigues, and litigation. Grimthorpe received no payment and had been far-sighted enough to have a contract at the beginning giving him real power, with the result, he said, '. . . every possible attempt was made to get rid of both it and me. No official who joined in those attempts cared three half-pence how the clock was made. Luckily I did care. . . .' The final cost of the clock including £750 for recasting Big Ben, the bell, was under £6,000. The cost of the iron frame provided by the architect was about £6,600! The clock was set working in 1859 and proved the most accurate large clock ever made. It has Grimthorpe's GRAVITY ESCAPEMENT, and a TWO SECONDS PENDULUM weighing about 700 lb. The three weights for timekeeping, striking and chiming, weigh 1½ cwt., 1½ tons, and 1½ tons respectively. The MOVEMENT looks like an elderly printing press and is 16 ft. long by 5 ft. 6 in. wide. Since 1913 it has been wound electrically. Winding by hand used to take over 30 hours a week. At one stage, Grimthorpe considered AUTOMATIC WINDING operated by the weight of people walking over Westminster Bridge. It is connected

194

electrically to the ROYAL OBSERVATORY for time checking and also to the firm of E. Dent & Co., who still look after it. The dials are nearly 22½ ft. in diameter, the centres being 180 ft. from the ground. The minute hands are 14 ft. long and weigh 2 cwt. each. The minute spaces are one foot square. Until 1900 the dials were lit by gas burners; now lighting is fluorescent.

Wetherfield Collection   Famous collection of clocks, containing the 'RECORD' TOMPION, amassed by David Wetherfield, a coal merchant, over 30 years, and offered for auction in 1928 after his death, but sold privately to Francis Mallet and Percy WEBSTER for £30,000.

Wheel   One of the larger gears in a watch or clock; usually made of brass and pierced to give it four spokes, called 'crossings'. The teeth of small gears are of cycloidal form because the common involute gear is unsuccessful on a small scale. *See* **Pinion.**

Wheel Barometer   Mercury barometer in which a small weight on a cord over a wheel rested on the surface of the mercury and turned a hand over a dial. Early clockmakers also made barometers.

Willard H. Wheeler Collection   U.S.A. private watch collection sold at Sothebys, London, for a total of £27,760 in 1961.

Wilsdorf Collection   The collection of ENAMELLED WATCHES made by H. Wilsdorf in Geneva.

Winding Button   The button or 'crown' of a watch used for winding and hand setting through the KEYLESS work.

Winding Square   Square-ended ARBOR to take a winding key. Winding was through the centre of the single hand on early watches, then through a hole in the dial, but this was superseded by KEYLESS WINDING. Some weight clocks and all spring clocks have winding squares in the dial or on the back of the MOVE-MENT, one for the GOING TRAIN, one for STRIKING, and one for CHIMING. Some clock-winding holes had grooved, decorative rings around them, once supposed (wrongly) to assist drunken clock winders! *See* **Tipsy Key.**

Wooden Clock   Clock with main parts of wood, including the PLATES, WHEELS and DIAL. The earliest were probably BLACK FOREST CLOCKS from about 1680. The first PRECISION CLOCK made by James or John HARRISON, in Yorkshire, was wooden and was claimed to keep time to one second a month for 10 years! Mass production of cheap wooden clocks was started in the U.S.A. in 1809 by Eli TERRY, Seth THOMAS, and Silas Hoadley. These were often sold without cases, which were added by local cabinet makers. Terry even made wooden TOWER CLOCKS, one being in the Congregational Church at Terryville, Connecticut. There is a Russian wooden watch in the Zwinger Museum, Dresden.

Woodpecker Escapement   Form of PIN WHEEL ESCAPEMENT in some early nineteenth century Austrian clocks to provide DEAD BEAT seconds with a half-seconds PENDULUM. One of two impulse PALLETS is hinged to prevent IMPULSE in one direction. Also called 'coup perdu'.

World Clock   Clock with a WORLD TIME DIAL. Often included in ASTRONOMICAL CLOCKS. There is a clock in the Zwinger Museum, Dresden, made in 1690 by Andreas Gartner, which shows the time in all latitudes on 360 supplementary dials!

World Time Dial   Clock or watch showing time of day in different parts of the world. As the Earth turns in 24 hrs., an hour hand turning once in this time over a 24-hr. dial is necessary. The main countries or towns of the world are marked round the BEZEL or an extra dial, that can be rotated. If the timepiece is in London and showing the time there, the bezel is turned by hand until the point on it marked 'London' is opposite the hour hand. To know the hour in another place, it is then only necessary to read it on the 24-hr. dial opposite the place name. As TIME ZONES vary by whole hours, an ordinary minute hand will give minutes for all zones, i.e. if it is 16.20 hr. G.M.T. in London, it is 11.20 in New York, 17.20 in Paris, and 19.20 in Leningrad. Several countries, including India and Central Australia, vary by half an hour from the Standard Time, however; an adjustment must be made for this, as well as for local variations such as BRITISH SUMMER TIME. Another form of world time dial is to have a model of the globe, or a drum or band carrying a map, revolving once in 24 hrs. A stationary ring around the equator is marked in hours from 1 to 24, so the place is found on the globe, the time there read on the ring, and the adjustment made for local variations of time zones, which can also be marked on the globe. Other versions are a stationary map of the world with a moving band indicating the hours, and a stationary map with actual time in DIGITAL INDICATION on the main countries in numerals.

Wrist-Chronometer   A wrist-watch that has obtained a RATING CERTIFICATE according to the Swiss definition.

Wrist-Watch   A watch was very occasionally worn attached to the wrist by ladies of the eighteenth century as a novelty. C. Girard Perregaux made Swiss wrist-watches for German Naval Officers in 1880, but did not put them on the market until after 1904. Benson introduced them in England in 1885, but they did not begin to be popular until about 1910. They were thought to be effeminate, but the First World War gave them a big stimulus when soldiers found them really practical. Many special wrist-watch STRAPS were made to hold small pocket watches. More and more special MOVEMENTS and CASES were designed, however, until today the world output of wrist-watches is 86 million yearly.

Year Clock   Clock that runs for a year at one winding. The most famous is a spring-driven striking and chiming clock made for King William III by TOMPION, which has had only three owners. A record is kept of all who wind it. Tested in 1950, its efficiency was found still to be much higher than modern clocks. A German firm makes a clock that runs five years on a torch battery.

Zaandam Clock   A DUTCH CLOCK made in Zaandam, where clockmakers worked, as well as in Friesland, in the seventeenth century.

Zodiac   The band of sky through which the Sun, Moon and planets appear to move. It is divided into twelve angles of 30° known by their 'signs' and sometimes shown on ASTRONOMICAL CLOCKS.

OTHER BOOKS TO READ

THIS book is the first Dictionary of Clocks and Watches to be published for the general reader. Those whose appetites for horology it has whetted might like to delve deeper. Here are some recommended books that are still (1961) in print:

In the same field

Watch & Clock Encyclopaedia, by Donald de Carle (N.A.G. Press, 50s). First rate and covers a very wide field, technical, antiquarian, and commercial, with over 1,000 illustrations.

Watch & Clockmakers Handbook, Dictionary and Guide, by F. J. Britten (Spon, 63s). The trade's 'bible', first published in 1878, but brought up to date; much design and working method information.

General History of Timekeeping

Time Measurement—Part I, by F. A. B. Ward (H.M. Stationery Office, 5s 6d). There is nothing to beat this concise summary for authority and facts.

Antiquarian Reference Books

Watchmakers & Clockmakers of the World, by G. H. Baillie (N.A.G. Press, 40s). Indispensable list of 36,000 clock and watchmakers with localities and dates, up to 1825.

Clocks & Watches—an Historical Bibliography, by G. H. Baillie (N.A.G. Press, 42s). Exceptional series of illustrated abstracts from the entire literature of horology—for those who want to get their facts right.

Technical

Electrical Timekeeping, by F. Hope-Jones (N.A.G. Press, 21s). The standard work on the subject, written with outstanding clarity by the man who thought of the 'six pips'.

The Science of Clocks and Watches, by A. L. Rawlings (Pitman, 20*s*). The only book that treats horology mathematically and is still readable.

Some of the antiquarian books below are also inclined to be technical.

For Antiquarians and Collectors
Some Outstanding Clocks over Seven Hundred Years, 1250–1950, by H. Alan Lloyd (Leonard Hill, 70*s*). Outstanding book, too —recommended to everyone interested in mechanisms.
Britten's Old Clocks & Watches & their Makers, by G. H. Baillie, C. Clutton and C. A. Ilbert (Spon, 7 gns.). An old classic, thoroughly revised, and extending over the entire antiquarian field.
The Grandfather Clock, by Ernest L. Edwardes (John Sherratt, 25*s*). Full of information on the subject not found elsewhere.
Old Clocks—Practical Handbook for Collectors, by Alan Lloyd (Benn, 30*s*). Very good exposition, with a large selection of pictures.
The Longcase Clock, by Eric Bruton (Arco, 12*s* 6*d*). A lucid introduction on the popular level for collectors.
Uhren, by Bassermann-Jordan/Bertele (Klinkhardt & Biermann, D.M. 76). Those who read German will find nothing better anywhere in the wider history of clocks and watches, especially for illustrations.
The Story of Watches, by T. P. Camerer Cuss (MacGibbon & Kee, 25*s*). The only general book on the subject—and at a popular price—since Baillie's massive classic *Watches*.

Practical Repairing
Practical Watch Repairing, by D. de Carle (N.A.G. Press, 30*s*). It is enough to say that a hundred thousand people have read this.

Practical Clock Repairing, by D. de Carle (N.A.G. Press, 30*s*). Good companion to the book above.

Modern Clocks, by T. R. Robinson (N.A.G. Press, 30*s*). Particularly interesting book on design, faults and their rectification.

Clocks at Sea

The Marine Chronometer, by R. T. Gould (Holland Press, 6 gns.). The standard work on the subject. Readable yet extremely well documented.

More Popular Reading

The True Book About Clocks, by Eric Bruton (Muller, 8*s* 6*d*). Unusual history describing personalities and feuds as well as inventions.

On the Fringe

Musical Boxes, by John E. T. Clark (Geo. Allen & Unwin, 42*s*). Excellent reading for anyone who likes clockwork.

CORRESPONDENCE COURSES IN HOROLOGY

THE only ones of their kind, they teach practical skill as well as theory, and are run without profit to increase knowledge of the subject. The Secretary, British Horological Institute, 35 Northampton Square, London, E.C.1, will send a syllabus.

DATE DUE			